maths
CHALLENGE

Edited by Tony Gardiner

2

OXFORD

OXFORD
UNIVERSITY PRESS

Great Clarendon Street, Oxford OX2 6DP

Oxford University Press is a department of the University of Oxford. It furthers the University's objective of excellence in research, scholarship, and education by publishing worldwide in

Oxford New York

Auckland Cape Town Dar es Salaam Hong Kong Karachi
Kuala Lumpur Madrid Melbourne Mexico City Nairobi
New Delhi Shanghai Taipei Toronto

with offices in

Argentina Austria Brazil Chile Czech Republic France
Greece Guatemala Hungary Italy Japan South Korea
Poland Portugal Singapore Switzerland Thailand Turkey
Ukraine Vietnam

Oxford is a registered trade mark of Oxford University Press
in the UK and in certain other countries

The materials were written, tested and revised over a period of several years by a group of practising teachers. The main contributors were: Tony Burghall, Peter Critchley, Michael Darby, Tony Gardiner, Bob Hartman, Mark Patmore, Diana Sharvill, Rosemary Tenison. They acknowledge additional contributions from Geoff Dunne and Peter Ransom. The final draft benefitted from scrutiny by Peter Moody. The moral rights of the authors have been asserted.

Throughout the development phase, the group's work was supported by the School Mathematics Project.

Database right Oxford University Press (maker)

First published 2000

10 9 8 7 6

British Library Cataloguing in Publication Data. Data available.

ISBN 0 19 914778 7

Typeset in Great Britain by Tradespools
Printed in Great Britain by Bell & Bain Ltd.

CHALLENGES

COMMENTS & SOLUTIONS

GLOSSARY

About this book

This book is the second in a series of three books covering Years 7–10 aimed at the top 10% or so of pupils aged 11–15. The series has been written and produced so that successive volumes provide an enrichment programme for the most able pupils in the lower secondary school, though many items could be adapted for use with other age groups and with a wider ability range. Where pupils are working mainly on their own, they will get more out of what Book 2 has to offer if they have first tackled a good part of the material in Book 1. Each individual section in this book can also be used to form the basis of an excellent 'masterclass' for secondary pupils.

Each book in the series contains twenty or more sections together with Comments and Solutions. These Comments and Solutions provide more than just a convenient way for pupils to check their answers: they have been written to help provoke further thought and discussion with peers or with a teacher. Teachers may have to stress that, even when pupils think they have succeeded in solving a problem, it is important for them to reflect on the approach they have used (and the reason why it works). In particular, they should never be satisfied with merely getting the answer.

The material has been extensively trialled and revised in the light of teachers' comments. The styles of the different sections are very varied. This provides a freshness of approach, which not only adds to the value of the collection, but which challenges pupils to think about familiar topics in new ways. Though different items are written in different styles, all sections seek to challenge able pupils in ways that will help them to:

*   develop a deeper understanding of the ideas and methods which are central to secondary mathematics

*   lay a firmer foundation for later work

*   develop reasoning skills

*   cultivate a broader interest in mathematics

*   develop their ability to research and to interpret mathematics.

The potential of the material is illustrated by three comments from teachers who trialled one batch of draft material.

'Excellent item on a topic that is rarely understood in depth.'

'If only my A-level students had seen this in Year 7!'

'This item is nicely constructed in a way which makes it suitable for either individuals or small groups working on their own.'

Other materials and strategies which are currently used to extend more able pupils tend either to provide interesting 'time-fillers' which have little to do with ordinary curriculum work, or to accelerate pupils through the National Curriculum levels (and the associated examinations) ahead of their peers. In contrast, this book contains activities which encourage pupils to think more deeply about relatively elementary mainstream material while covering a fairly broad range of standard curriculum topics. The book also includes some extension material which enriches the standard curriculum. Thus it offers schools an alternative both to using time-fillers, and to the acceleration strategy referred to above (a strategy which puts considerable burdens on staff, and which leads to able pupils being permanently out of phase with their peers).

Contents

How to use this book

To teachers and parents

- This book is aimed at pupils with the same kind of background as the top 10% of pupils in Years 8–9 in English schools (i.e. pupils aged 12–14). It is the first of a series of three books containing material to challenge and extend such pupils in Years 7–10 (aged 11–15).

- To get the most out of what Book 2 has to offer, pupils should first tackle a good part of Book 1.

- Many of the sections included can be completed by pupils working on their own; the **Comments and Solutions** provide additional support. However, all sections would benefit from some discussion – either with other pupils as part of the activity, or with a teacher or parent.

- A brief summary of the intended learning objectives is given at the beginning of each section, along with the intended classroom organisation (whether individual, or small group work), any necessary materials which must be available, and any sections which should have been tackled before you start.

  This information is provided both to help the experienced teacher, who may be using the material for the first time, and to alert pupils to any necessary prerequisites.

- When pupils do not understand a technical term which appears in the text, they should first consult the **Glossary** at the back of the book.

- The amount of time a given pupil spends on each section will vary. However, we anticipate that each shorter section should take 45–60 minutes, while each longer section may take 1–2 hours.

- Some sections explicitly tell pupils to *choose* a task which interests them, rather than to attempt every single task. Even where pupils are expected to work systematically through a section, it is not essential for them to complete every single question.

How to use this book

To pupils

- These activities challenge you to think more seriously about some of the mathematics you have learned, and about the way you do mathematics. This will not only improve what you can do this year, but will help to lay a solid foundation for future work.

- To get the most out of what Book 2 has to offer, you should first tackle a good part of Book 1.

- Some problems are straightforward; other problems are rather hard. Don't give up too easily. If the last couple of questions in a section are too difficult, or involve ideas which you have not yet met, don't worry. It is more important to think carefully about the problems you do than to worry about the ones you leave undone.

- **You are not expected to tackle every single section!** Nor do you have to complete every single question in the sections you do tackle. The material is meant to be fun – as well as being challenging. So if you have to choose, concentrate on those items that interest you most. However, a problem will often not make sense unless you have understood earlier problems in the same section; so **make sure you complete the first few questions in each section** that you tackle.

- Many of the sections can be completed on your own. Some require you to talk to someone else about the ideas involved. It can often help to talk things through with someone else, even when it is not strictly needed in order to complete the task.

- Some sections may require you to visit a library or to use reference books. In addition there is a **Glossary** (that is, a mini-dictionary) at the end of the book which should help to explain any unfamiliar mathematical words or symbols which are used in the text.

- The **Comments and Solutions** are included to help you. Use them wisely! Don't peep too soon; but don't be afraid to use them to help you get unstuck. If you struggle to understand the Comments and Solutions for one question in a section, it will often help you to tackle other questions in that section.

  Remember that the most important thing is not just to get 'the answer. You should always present the method you use in a way that shows that it is correct. In mathematics this often means that a full solution to a problem has to use algebra!

1 *Does it go? How do you know?*

This activity focuses on:

- investigating tests for divisibility;
- understanding and using place value;
- writing out careful explanations and proofs.

Organisation/Before you start:

- You need to know how to multiply out brackets.
- You may need access to books containing information on divisibility tests.

Read this passage carefully. Then answer the questions.

An integer in the Hindu-Arabic numeral system is a multiple of 10 when its units digit is equal to 0. In general, the units digit of a number gives the remainder when you divide the number by 10. For example,

$$1234 = 1×1000 + 2×100 + 3×10 + \underline{4}$$
$$= 10(1×100 + 2 × 10 + 3) + \underline{4}$$
$$= multiple\ of\ 10 \qquad\qquad + \underline{4}$$

This useful observation depends on the fact that 10, 100, 1000 are all multiples of 10.

The numbers $10 - 1 = 9$, $100 - 1 = 99$, $1000 - 1 = 999$ are all multiples of 9. You can use this fact to tell very easily what the remainder will be when you divide an integer by 9, without actually doing the division. For example,

$$1234 = \underline{1}×1000 + \underline{2}×100 + \underline{3}×10 + \underline{4}$$
$$= \underline{1}(999 + 1) + \underline{2}(99 + 1) + \underline{3}(9 + 1) + \underline{4}$$
$$= (1×999 + 2×99 + 3×9) + (\underline{1} + \underline{2} + \underline{3} + \underline{4}).$$
$$= (multiple\ of\ 9)\ +\ (sum\ of\ the\ digits).$$

So the remainder when you divide 1234 by 9 is the same as the remainder when you divide the digit sum $1 + 2 + 3 + 4$ by 9: in this case 1.

1 How can you tell when an integer is exactly divisible

  a by 100

  b by 1000?

  Explain each answer carefully.

2 How can you tell when an integer is exactly divisible

    a by 5?

    b by 25?

    Explain each answer carefully.

3 How can you tell when an integer is exactly divisible by

    a by 2?

    b by 4?

    c by 8?

    Explain each answer carefully.

4 Without using a calculator and without doing any written divisions, find the remainder when each of these numbers is divided by 9.

    a 123 456

    b 1 234 567

    c 12 345 678

    d 123 456 789

5 **a** Write down a simple way of deciding **at a glance** whether a given number is divisible by 3. Prove that your method is correct.

    b Decide, without doing any written calculation, which of the numbers 123, 1234, 12 345, 123 456, 1 234 567 are divisible by 3. How can you tell at a glance which of these numbers are divisible by 6?

6 Look up divisibility tests for other divisors such as 11 and 7.

2 True, False and 'Iffy' shape statements

This activity focuses on:

- logical thinking;
- making precise statements;
- identifying and resolving common mistakes involving shapes.

Organisation/Before you start:

- This section is best tackled by two or three pupils working together. (If you are working on your own, imagine how you would convince others that your decisions are correct.)

Some of the statements on the next page are **Definitely true**; others are **Definitely false**; and some are **'Iffy'** (true if …).
An **'Iffy'** statement is one that is not true as it stands, but which could become true if it was made more precise.
For example: The statement

The diagonal of a rectangle is a line of symmetry

is **'Iffy'**, because it is false for most rectangles (such as a long thin rectangle), and is only true if the rectangle happens to be a square.

1 **a** Make copies of the statements **A–P** on the next page and cut them out so that you have each statement on a separate slip of paper.

b Make a table with four columns headed like this:

Definitely true	'Iffy'	Definitely false	Don't know

The **Definitely true** column should be about half a page wide.
The other columns should be about one sixth of a page wide.

c Pick one of the statements **A–P**.
Decide which column it should go in and put it there.
Only use the **Don't know** column if you do not understand the statement, or if you cannot decide where it should go.
(**Remember**: 'Iffy' is not the same as **Don't know**.)
Repeat this for each of the statements **A–P**.

d Now pick one of the statements that you put in the **'Iffy'** column.

Try to make the statement more precise so that your improved version could go in the **Definitely true** column.

For example, to make the statement

The diagonal of a rectangle is a line of symmetry.

more precise so that it becomes **Definitely true**, we could change it to

The diagonal of a *square* is a line of symmetry.

or

If the diagonal of a rectangle is a line of symmetry,
then the rectangle must be a square.

Do this for each statement you put in the '**Iffy**' column.

e Ask your teacher about any statements in your **Don't know** column.

A All squares are rectangles.	B A triangle can have two obtuse angles.
C The diagonals of a rectangle cross at right angles.	D If *A* is 20 cm from *B* and *B* is 10 cm from *C*, then *A* is 30 cm from *C*.
E When you double the sides of a square you double the area.	F A parallelogram has rotation symmetry of order 4.
G A parallelogram is a rectangle.	H Doubling the radius of a circle doubles its area.
I Every quadrilateral can be used to tesselate the plane.	J The longest side of a triangle is shorter than the sum of the lengths of the other two sides.
K If two rectangles both have area 24 cm², they must also have the same perimeter.	L Cutting a kite along a diagonal produces two congruent triangles.
M A rhombus is a parallelogram.	N Four straight lines cross at six different points.
O If two lines are perpendicular to a third line, they must be parallel to each other.	P Any parallelogram can be cut into two pieces which fit together to make a rectangle.

3 *Counting back in time*

This activity focuses on:

- exploring different counting systems and numeral systems;
- comprehension of information given in text form.

Organisation/Before you start:

- You may need access to reference books that contain lists of counting words in other languages.

Read the passage below carefully before you try to answer the questions.

The spoken words we use for numbers developed slowly. At first there was no fixed counting sequence **one**, **two**, **three**, **four**, *... which could be used whenever there was a need to count something, and which was the same for all objects. For example, in the Fiji Islands, the word* **bola** *is used for ten boats, and a quite different word* **koro** *is used to refer to ten coconuts. In English we still use special words for certain numbers of special objects, such as a* **brace** *of pheasants (meaning two pheasants). These special words add colour to the language. However there are great advantages in being able to use the same word* **two** *every time – together with the name for the objects being counted:* **two** *pheasants,* **two** *boats,* **two** *coconuts, etc. – rather than having to use a completely different word each time.*

The earliest evidence of human counting is from the marks scratched on old **tally sticks**. *A tally stick is a stick or bone which was used to record the result of counting some important collection of objects (such as sheep, or cattle, or slaves). Five objects would be represented by five vertical marks or scratches* |||||. *This simple process of making tally marks was improved by grouping the marks – often in fives. One common way of doing this is to scratch the fifth mark in each group of five* **across** *the previous four to create an easily seen group of five like this:* ‖‖.

A further improvement was the introduction of special symbols to stand for particular numbers. The Egyptians used | *for one,* ∩ *for ten. To make things easier still, they grouped the symbols together so that one could see at a glance what number was being represented. For example, our number* **thirty four** *would be written as* ∩∩∩ ||||. *The*

Romans used certain capital letters as number symbols: I stood for one, V for five, X for ten, and so on.

Any method of writing numbers using symbols rather than words is called a **numeral system**. A good numeral system should be systematic, and should make it just as easy to write unfamiliar large numbers as it is to write familiar small numbers. A good numeral system should also make it relatively easy to do arithmetic.

Tally marks are certainly systematic; but they make it very hard to work with large numbers. Roman numerals are better for writing large numbers, but they are not systematic: for example, it is not clear whether the Roman numeral for ninety nine should be LXXXXVIIII, or LXXXXIX, or XCIX. Roman numerals also make arithmetic rather awkward.

Nowadays we use the modern Hindu-Arabic numeral system. This is systematic, allows us to write large numbers just as easily as small numbers, and makes arithmetic relatively straightforward. It also extends naturally to decimals. When writing numerals systematically in **base 10**, the meaning of each digit depends on its position: for example, in **base 10**,

364 stands for 3 hundreds, 6 tens and 4 units.

One of the most important features of our numeral system is the humble zero, 0. Without it we could not distinguish between 37 (3 tens and 7 units) and 307 (3 hundreds, 0 tens and 7 units).

It is sometimes possible to see traces of the way people used to count in the words they still use for numbers. You can see some examples in the table opposite. Words for numbers in Chinese, as in English, are based on the number ten. However, in English we have the occasional minor variation, such as thirteen and fifteen, rather than three-teen and five-teen; there are also historical exceptions, such as eleven and twelve, instead of one-teen and two-teen.

Number	Language		
	Chinese	**Aztec**	**Traditional Welsh**
1	i	ce	un
2	erh	ome	dau
3	san	yey	tri
4	szu	naui	pedwar
5	wu	macuilli	pump
6	liu	chic-ce	chwech
7	ch'i	chic-ome	saith
8	pa	chic-yey	wyth
9	chiu	chic-naui	naw
10	shih	matlacti	deg
11	shih-i	matlacti-on-ce	un ar ddeg
12	shih-erh	matlacti-on-ome	deuddeg
13	shih-san	matlacti-on-yey	tri ar ddeg
14	shih-szu	matlacti-on-naui	pedwar ar ddeg
15	shih-wu	caxtulli	pymtheg
16	shih-liu	caxtulli-on-ce	un ar bymtheg
17	shih-ch'i	caxtulli-on-ome	dau ar bymtheg
18	shih-pa	caxtulli-on-yey	deunaw
19	shih-chiu	caxtulli-on-naui	pedwar ar bymtheg
20	erh-shih	cem-poualli	ugain
30	san-shih	cem-poualli-om-matlacti	deg ar hugain
40	szu-shih	ome-poualli	deugain
60	liu-shih	yey-poualli	trigain
80	pa-shih	naui-poualli	pedwar ugain

1 **a** What patterns can you find in the number words listed in the table? Investigate all three languages.

  b In what ways are Chinese and English similar? In what ways are they different?

  c In what ways are Aztec and Welsh similar? In what ways are they different?

2 Choose another language (other than English, Chinese, Aztec, or Welsh). Make a list of the number words for 1–19, 20, 30, 40, and for 10 000 and 100 000. In what ways is your chosen language like English, or Chinese, or Aztec, or Welsh?

3 How many different English words can you find, like pair or brace, that are used to refer to **two** of something?

4 Which single English word has all three of these meanings?

- twenty

- to scratch a mark on card

- to get the ball in the net.

5 In Egyptian hieroglyphics 9 stands for 100, and $\overset{\text{c}}{\underset{\lambda}{\text{l}}}$ stands for 1000.

  a What number does $9∩∩|||$ stand for?

  b Write *one thousand two hundred and thirty four* in hieroglyphics.

6 What events happened

  a in the year MCCCCLXXXXII?

  b in the year MDCCLXXVI?

7 Write down two Roman numerals other than the three given in the passage above which could logically stand for *ninety nine*.

8 Write out the number 1 234 567 890 987 654 321 in English words.

4 *Fractions bits and pieces*

This activity focuses on:

• exploring properties of fractions.

Organisation/Before you start:

• You need to work with the arithmetic of fractions without converting to decimals.

Choose two or three of the five tasks that look interesting. Then work through them carefully. Do not use a calculator.

Subtract one

1 Write down a fraction greater than $\frac{1}{2}$ and less than 1.

• Subtract 1 from both the numerator and the denominator to get a new fraction.

• Repeat this with your new fraction: subtract 1 from the numerator and from the denominator to get another new fraction.

• Keep reducing the numerator and denominator by 1 each time to form a sequence of new fractions.
Do you eventually reach a fraction which is equivalent to $\frac{1}{2}$? How many steps does it take?

2 a If you start with a different fraction between $\frac{1}{2}$ and 1 and repeatedly subtract 1 from both the numerator and the denominator, will you always reach a fraction that is equivalent to $\frac{1}{2}$? How can you be sure?

b Can you predict in advance how many steps it will take?

On and on forever

3 $1 + \frac{1}{2} = \frac{3}{2}$, and $1 + \frac{1}{2} + \frac{1}{4} = \frac{7}{4}$.
What would the answer be if you could keep on adding for ever in this sum?

$$1 + \frac{1}{2} + \frac{1}{4} + \frac{1}{8} + \frac{1}{16} + \frac{1}{32} + \frac{1}{64} + \frac{1}{128} + \ldots = ?$$

4 What would the answer be if this sum went on for ever?

$$1 - \frac{1}{2} + \frac{1}{4} - \frac{1}{8} + \frac{1}{16} - \frac{1}{32} + \frac{1}{64} - \frac{1}{128} + \ldots = ?$$

Egyptian fractions

A **unit fraction** has numerator equal to 1, like $\frac{1}{3}$ or $\frac{1}{123}$.
The Ancient Egyptians were happy using unit fractions. They were less happy with general fractions. So whenever they had to work with a fraction like $\frac{3}{4}$, they would write it as a sum of different unit fractions:

$$\frac{3}{4} = \frac{1}{2} + \frac{1}{4}, \quad \text{or} \quad \frac{5}{6} = \frac{1}{2} + \frac{1}{3}, \quad \text{or} \quad \frac{59}{70} = \frac{1}{2} + \frac{1}{5} + \frac{1}{7}.$$

5 Write each of these fractions as the sum of different unit fractions:

  a $\frac{7}{8}$ **b** $\frac{7}{12}$ **c** $\frac{10}{13}$

  Which of these can be done in more than one way?

6 Can every proper fraction be written as a sum of different unit fractions?

Sums and products

7 The two numbers 3 and $1\frac{1}{2}$ have the curious property that their **sum** $3 + 1\frac{1}{2}$ is equal to their **product** $3 \times 1\frac{1}{2}$.
  Find some other pairs of numbers with the same property.

8 Can you find a way of describing **all** pairs of numbers with this property?

Consecutive digits

Using the consecutive digits 6, 7, 8 you can make fractions like $\frac{6}{78}$, $\frac{6}{87}$ and $\frac{8}{76}$. Each of these fractions simplifies: $\frac{6}{78} = \frac{1}{13}$, $\frac{6}{87} = \frac{2}{29}$ and $\frac{8}{76} = \frac{2}{19}$.

9 Choose a string of **consecutive** digits from 0–9 and try to make each of the unit fractions $\frac{1}{2}, \frac{1}{3}, \frac{1}{4}, \frac{1}{5}, \frac{1}{6}, \frac{1}{7}, \frac{1}{8}, \frac{1}{9}$.
  For example, to make $\frac{1}{2}$ you have to choose consecutive digits and then arrange them to make the numerator and denominator of a fraction that simplifies to give $\frac{1}{2}$.

10 Can you find a way of making one of the fractions $\frac{1}{2}, \frac{1}{3}, \frac{1}{4}, \frac{1}{5}, \frac{1}{6}, \frac{1}{7}, \frac{1}{8}, \frac{1}{9}$ that uses up all ten digits 0–9? Can you make one of these fractions using a string of nine consecutive digits?

5 BIG names

CHALLENGES

Read this short passage before trying to answer the questions that follow it.

In the margin is a list of English number names together with the numbers that they represent. The old meanings were widely accepted until 20 or so years ago; these old meanings are still standard in some languages (such as German). In the English speaking world the old usage has been largely replaced by the new. Only the first three names are widely used.

Name	Old	New
Million	10^6	10^6
Billion	10^{12}	10^9
Trillion	10^{18}	10^{12}
Quadrillion	10^{24}	10^{15}
Quintillion	10^{30}	10^{18}
Sextillion	10^{36}	10^{21}
Septillion	10^{42}	10^{24}
Octillion	10^{48}	10^{27}
Nonillion	10^{54}	10^{30}
Decillion	10^{60}	10^{33}
Undecillion	10^{66}	10^{36}
Duodecillion	10^{72}	10^{39}
Tredecillion	10^{78}	10^{42}
Quattuordecillion	10^{84}	10^{45}
Quindecillion	10^{90}	10^{48}
Sexdecillion	10^{96}	10^{51}
Septendecillion	10^{102}	10^{54}
Octodecillion	10^{108}	10^{57}
Novemdecillion	10^{114}	10^{60}
Vigintillion	10^{120}	10^{63}

Powers of 10

1 If you know the power of 10 for a number in the new system, how do you work out the power of 10 for the number with the same name in the old system?

2 Each number name has a different prefix. What patterns or rules can you find to help work out which power of 10 is represented by each number name

• in the old system?

• in the new system?

a How are the powers of 10 related to the prefixes in the old system?

b How are the powers of 10 related to the prefixes in the new system?

3 What would you expect the value (as a power of 10) of a **centrillion** to be in each of the two systems?

Notation

4 The old system has some advantages: for example,

$$(\text{a quadrillion}) \times (\text{a quintillion}) = \text{a nonillion}.$$

a Why is this an advantage? Is there a pattern that allows you to predict the name for the product of two numbers in the old system?

b What happens in the new system?

5 What do you expect to be the answer to

$$(\text{a sextillion}) \times (\text{a septillion})$$

a in the old system?

b in the new system?

Names

6 Find out about the numbers

a a gillion

b a googol

c a googolplex.

7 The Ancient Greeks did not write numbers using powers of 10. This made it much more difficult for them to think about large numbers. Archimedes (died 212 BC) wrote *The Sandreckoner* for King Hieron to show that the number of grains of sand in the universe must be finite. To do this he showed that there cannot possibly be more than N grains of sand in the universe. Find out how big Archimedes' number N was (as a power of 10).

6 Quadrilaterals

This activity focuses on:

- reinforcing the vocabulary associated with quadrilaterals;
- thinking about the connections between different kinds of quadrilaterals;
- finding out things related to quadrilaterals.

Organisation/Before you start:

- You will need access to books containing information on the geometry of quadrilaterals and on the history of mathematics.

1 What is the mathematical definition of the word **quadrilateral?**

2 Look up the word quadrilateral in a dictionary and find out as much as you can about

   a the origin of the word, and

   b how the different parts of the word contribute to its meaning.

3 Some schools and colleges have quads: a famous example is the 'Tom Quad' in Christ Church College, Oxford. The word quad is short for **quadrangle**. Look up the word quadrangle. What is the origin of the word? What do the different bits of the word tell you about its meaning?
   Does quadrangle have the same meaning as quadrilateral?

4 **a** Write down the names of all the different types of quadrilateral you can think of.

   b Write down the mathematical definition of each type of quadrilateral you listed in part **a**.

5 There are all sorts of interesting and important connections between the kinds of quadrilateral you listed in question **4**: for example, the first two types of quadrilateral you met in primary school were squares and rectangles, and a square is a special kind of rectangle. Write down as many connections as you can think of between different kinds of quadrilateral.

6 **a** One good way of presenting your answer to question **5** would be to represent the different kinds of quadrilateral in a **Venn diagram**. Make sure you know what a Venn diagram is. Find out as much as you can about **John Venn** after whom they are named.

b Represent your answer to question **5** using a single Venn diagram.

7 **a** Draw a large trapezium. Mark the midpoint of each side as accurately as you can. Join these four points to make a new quadrilateral. What kind of quadrilateral do you think this new quadrilateral is?

b Draw a quadrilateral that is not a trapezium. Mark the midpoint of each side and join these four points to make a new quadrilateral. What do you notice?

c I start with a quadrilateral, mark the midpoints and join them up to make a new quadrilateral. My new quadrilateral is a rhombus. What kind of quadrilateral do you think I started with?

8 **a** Given a triangle ABC, let M, N be the midpoints of the two sides AB and BC. Find out what **The Midpoint Theorem** tells you about the line segment MN.

b How does this help explain what you found in question **7**?

EXTRA 1

Centrefold

A square piece of paper is folded in half. The resulting rectangle has perimeter 12 cm. What was the area of the original square?

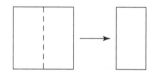

Solution: page 90

7 *Dozens of different ways of counting*

This activity focuses on:

- understanding and working with different number bases;
- factors (or divisors) and divisibility.

Organisation/Before you start:

- You will need access to suitable reference books.

Read this passage carefully. Then answer the questions which follow.

Counting

*In most everyday work we count in tens: that is, we work in **base 10**. When we write numbers in base 10, the column a digit is in tells you its value. The number column headings are:*

Thousands	Hundreds	Tens	Units
(1000)	*(100)*	*(10)*	*(1)*

*In the past, numbers have often been written in other number bases, sometimes using a mixture of number bases. For example, until 1971 British money involved pounds, shillings and pence: 12 pence made one shilling, and 20 shillings made one pound. Old-fashioned units of length (miles, furlongs, yards, feet and inches) were another example of a system which used mixed number bases starting with twelves: there were twelve inches in a foot. Many items used to be sold in dozens, or twelves. The word dozen is very like the French word **douze** for twelve, and comes from the Latin word for twelve, which is **duodecimo**. This itself comes from the Latin words **duo** (which means two) and **decem** (which means ten).*

One advantage of working in base 12 is that 12 has a lot of factors. Sets of 12 things can be divided up in different ways. In fact 12 is the smallest integer with six factors, including 1 and 12. The Duodecimal Society still publishes pamphlets explaining the benefits of using base 12 in everyday life.

Counting in twelves

If you try to count in base 12, the first four column headings are 'units', dozens, and so on, and their values (written in base 10!) are:

Name	??	?	Dozens	Units
Value	*1728*	*144*	*12*	*1*

There are no standard names for the first two columns (though the '144' column could be labelled 'grosses').

*Numbers less than 12 are written in the units column: they do not carry over into the dozens column. So we need two extra symbols to act as digits for 'ten' and for 'eleven'. We use D for ten (pronounced **dek**) and E for eleven (pronounced **el**). Thus numbers written in base 12 use the digits*

0, 1, 2, 3, 4, 5, 6, 7, 8, 9, D, E.

As soon as we get to twelve, the number carries over into the twelves column; so the number twelve is written 10 in base 12. Counting from zero to twenty five in base 12 goes like this:

 0, 1, 2, 3, 4, 5, 6, 7, 8, 9, D, E,
10, 11, 12, 13, 14, 15, 16, 17, 18, 19, 1D, 1E,
20, 21.

So in base 12:

10 *stands for the number* **twelve**;

20 *stands for the number* **twenty four**;

3D *stands for the number* **forty six** ($= 3 \times 12 + 10$).

In base 12 it is easy to test for small factors. For example,

- *a number has 2 as a factor precisely when its units digit is even;*

- *a number has 3 as a factor precisely when its units digit is 0, 3, 6, or 9.*

Ancient civilisations used numeral systems involving different number bases – though they usually mixed different bases in one system, like the old English units of length and weight. For example, the Babylonians used a system which was (partly) base 60; the Mayans used base 5, and the Aztecs used base 20.

1 a What are the factors of 12?

   b What are the factors of 10?

2 a What is the smallest integer with six factors (including itself and 1)?
   What is the next smallest integer with six factors?

   b What is the smallest integer with seven factors?

3 Write these base 12 numbers in base 10:

a 40   **b** D0   **c** 12D   **d** EE

4 Write these base 10 numbers in base 12:

a 60   **b** 100   **c** 240   **d** 142

5 **a** In the old-fashioned units for length how many inches were there in a foot? How many feet in a yard? How many yards in a furlong? How many furlongs in a mile?

b In the old-fashioned units for weight (tons, hundredweights, stones, pounds and ounces) how many ounces were there in a pound? How many pounds in a stone? How many stones in a hundredweight? How many hundredweights in a ton?

c Find out about **troy weights** (as used by goldsmiths and silversmiths). Why are they called 'troy' weights?

6 **a** The text at the beginning of this section gives a simple way to test whether a number written in base 12 has 2 or 3 as a factor. Explain why this method works.

b Write down a way to test whether a number written in base 12 has 4 as a factor. Explain why your method works.

c Find a way of testing whether a number written in base 12 has 6, or 8, or 9, or 12 as a factor.

7 Find out what a **gross** is.

8 Where do we use **base 60** in everyday life?

9 Find the origins of these mathematical words:

a score   **b** count   **c** pound   **d** ounce   **e** inch.

10 The Duodecimal Society publishes *The Duodecimal Bulletin*, giving the date (naturally!) in base 12. The first issue was published in the year 1161 (in base 12). What year was this in base 10?

11 Find out about the number bases which were used in old systems of measurement.

8 *True, False and 'Iffy' negative number statements*

This activity focuses on:

- logical thinking;
- making precise statements;
- identifying and resolving common mistakes involving negative numbers.

Some of the statements on the next page are **Definitely true**; others are **Definitely false**; and some are '**Iffy**' (true if ...).
An '**Iffy**' statement is one that is not true as it stands, but which could become true if it was made more precise.
For example: The statement

Two negatives make a positive

is '**Iffy**', because it is always false if you add two negative numbers but is true if you multiply (or divide) two negative numbers.

1 a Make copies of the statements **A–N** on the next page and cut them out so that you have each statement on a separate slip of paper.

b Make a table with four columns headed like this:

Definitely true	'Iffy'	Definitely false	Don't know

The **Definitely true** column should be about half a page wide.
The other columns should each be about one sixth of a page wide.

c Pick one of the statements **A–N**.
Decide which column it should go in and put it there.
Only use the **Don't know** column if you do not understand the statement, or if you cannot decide where it should go.
(**Remember:** '**Iffy**' is not the same as **Don't know**.)
Repeat this for each of the statements **A–N**.

d Now pick one of the statements that you put in the '**Iffy**' column.
Try to make the statement more precise so that your improved version could go in the **Definitely true** column.

For example, to make the statement

Two negatives make a positive

more precise so that it becomes **Definitely true**, you could change it to

Multiplying two negative *numbers gives a* positive *answer.*

Do this for each statement you put in the '**Iffy**' column.

e Ask your teacher about any statements in your **Don't know** column.

A When you add two negative numbers, the answer is positive.	**B** The sum of two numbers is always greater than their difference.
C Two negatives make a positive.	**D** If n is negative, then $\frac{1}{n}$ is less than $^-1$.
E When you add two negative numbers, the answer is negative.	**F** The product of two negative numbers is positive.
G Subtracting one negative number from another negative number gives a positive answer.	**H** When you add two numbers the total is greater than 0.
I When you add, you move to the right along the number line.	**J** If $a > b$, then $^-a > {}^-b$.
K Subtracting a positive number is the same as adding a negative number.	**L** The sum of a positive number and a negative number is negative.
M Adding a negative number is the same as subtracting a positive number.	**N** When you divide a positive number by a negative number the answer is positive.

9 *Could you?*

CHALLENGES

This activity focuses on:

- deciding what calculation to do to answer a numerical question;
- practising estimation;
- looking up numerical facts;
- working with units in context.

Organisation/Before you start:

- For some questions you will need access to suitable reference books.
- If you are working with a partner, pick some questions to work on individually, then explain your methods and conclusions to each other.

When answering these 'Could you ...?' questions, you should make sensible **estimates**, and then **calculate** efficiently. Do not just guess! The important part of this exercise is how you simplify the required calculation.

> The person answering these questions is assumed to be an ordinary human being with unlimited ability to organise, but no supernatural powers.

Could you ...

1 ... stand the whole population of the Earth on the Isle of Wight?

2 ... drink enough in a lifetime to empty a swimming pool?

3 ... fit a million grains of rice into an empty one litre container?

4 ... carry one kilometre of toilet paper without any help?

5 ... knit a jumper using just half a kilometre of wool?

6 ... drive in town at 10 metres per second?

7 ... wrap up a 150 mm×100 mm×100 mm box using a single A4 sheet of paper?

8 ... build a garage using no more than 1000 bricks?

9 ... tile the roof of a garage using only 1000 tiles?

10 ... find a cat that weighs more than five thousand paper clips?

10 *Fractions with a calculator*

This activity focuses on:

- the advantages of working with fractions;
- using your calculator to improve your understanding of fractions;
- working with fractions to improve the way you use your calculator.

Organisation/Before you start:

- You must be able to simplify fractions.
- You need to use a calculator to change fractions to decimals.
- You need to be prepared to think about recurring decimals.

1 **a** Which of the two fractions $\frac{5}{8}$ and $\frac{1}{3}$ do you think is the 'simplest'?

   b Use your calculator to change $\frac{5}{8}$ and $\frac{1}{3}$ to decimals. Write down the answer in the calculator display. What do you notice about the number of digits in each answer?

   c Do the same for $\frac{1}{4}, \frac{1}{5}, \frac{1}{6}, \frac{1}{7}$.
   What do you notice about the number of digits in each answer?

2 **a** What answer do you get if you take the decimal for $\frac{1}{3}$ from question **1b** and multiply it by 3?

   b Use your calculator to find the decimals for $\frac{1}{23}$ and for $\frac{2}{23}$.
   Write down the answers that appear in the display.
   The answer for $\frac{2}{23}$ should be exactly twice the answer for $\frac{1}{23}$.
   Is it?

3 Do not use your calculator for this question.

   a Work out the **exact** decimals for the fractions $\frac{1}{2}, \frac{1}{3}, \frac{1}{4}, \frac{1}{5}, \frac{1}{6}, \frac{1}{7}$.

   b How do the answers you found in part **a** differ from the answers you found in question **1b**, **c**? Why are the answers slightly different?

   c What happens if you multiply the **exact** decimal for $\frac{1}{3}$ by 3? What does this tell you about the decimal 'nought point nine recurring'?

In the first three questions you should have noticed that:

- the number of digits in the answer varies a lot: some awkward fractions have short decimals, and some simple-looking fractions produce very long decimals;

- the decimal answers on your calculator are often not exact;

- the decimal for some fractions stops (or **terminates**), but that for many simple fractions the exact decimal goes on for ever (**non-terminating**);

- the non-terminating decimal $0.9\dot{9} = 0.9999\ldots$ (for ever) is **exactly** equal to 1.

Decimals are often convenient, but they can be messy and inexact. In contrast, a fraction is **exact**, **concise** and **easy to grasp**. This is what makes fractions important.

Use your calculator to help you answer these questions.

4 **a** Add $\frac{11}{15}$ and $\frac{13}{18}$ as fractions. Give the answer in its simplest form. Write the answer as an improper fraction, and as a mixed number. Change this answer to a decimal.

b Change $\frac{11}{15}$ and $\frac{13}{18}$ into decimals. Write down the answers in the display. Add these two decimals.
Is your answer the same as for part **a**? If not, why do you think the answers are different?

5 What do your answers to questions **3** and **4** tell you about the effect of using decimals to carry out calculations involving fractions?

6 How does your calculator treat **non-terminating** decimals (like that for $\frac{1}{3}$)?

EXTRA 2

Spot the pattern

If this pattern is continued, which number will be directly below 100? Which number will be directly below 1000?

```
         1
      2  3  4
   5  6  7  8  9
10 11 12 13 14 15 16
 .  .  .  .  .  .  .  .
```

Solution: page 90

---

11 *Prove yourself*

This activity focuses on:

- using simple algebra to prove general results.

Organisation/Before you start:

- You need to know what a **magic square** is.

In each of the four challenges in this section there are three columns.
- The first (left-hand) column contains instructions in words.
- The second (middle) column contains a numerical example which follows the instructions line by line.
- The third (right-hand) column follows the numerical example using symbols, giving the full algebraic generalisation.

In each challenge your task is to:
- understand each step in the given worked example (middle column),
- see how the algebra is used (right-hand column), then use algebra to answer the questions at the end.

Start by working through the first challenge.

Calendar

Write down the days of the week.
Choose a day for the 1st of the month, and number the days from 1 to 31 as in a (long) calendar month.

Su	Mo	Tu	We	Th	Fr	Sa
			1	2	3	4
5	6	7	8	9	10	11
12	13	14	15	16	17	18
19	20	21	22	23	24	25
26	27	28	29	30	31	

Instructions	Numerical example	Algebraic generalisation
Choose a 3×3 square of numbers from your calendar. Draw a box round them.	Su Mo Tu **We Th Fr** Sa 1 2 3 4 5 6 7 |8 9 10| 11 12 13 14 |15 16 17| 18 19 20 21 |22 23 24| 25 26 27 28 29 30 31	$\begin{array}{lll} a & a+1 & a+2 \\ a+7 & a+8 & a+9 \\ a+14 & a+15 & a+16 \end{array}$
Add the numbers in the middle column: total C.	$C = 9 + 16 + 23$ $\quad = \mathbf{48}$	$C = a+1+a+8+a+15$ $\quad = \mathbf{3a + 24}$
Add the numbers in the middle row: total R.	$R = \underline{\quad\quad}$	$R = a+7+a+8+a+9$ $\quad = \underline{\quad\quad}$
Add up one diagonal: D_1.	$D_1 = \underline{\quad\quad}$	$D_1 = \underline{\quad\quad}$
Add the other diagonal: D_2.	$D_2 = \underline{\quad\quad}$	$D_2 = \underline{\quad\quad}$

> **Claim**: The four totals C, R, D_1, D_2 will always be the same no matter which 3×3 square you choose.
>
> **Proof**: All four expressions in the right-hand column are equal to $3a + 24$. **QED**

1   Prove that, no matter which 3×3 square you choose, the nine numbers in your 3×3 square can always be re-arranged to make a magic square.

Think of a number

Instructions	Numerical example	Algebraic generalisation
Write down any positive integer.	15	a
Multiply it by 3.	45	$3a$
Add 5.	50	$3a + 5$
Double the result.	100	$6a + 10$
Subtract 4.	96	$6a + 6$
Divide the result by 6.	16	$a + 1$
Subtract the original number.	**Answer** = ____	**Answer** = $a + 1 - a =$ ____

> **Claim**: No matter what number you start with, you always end up with 1.
>
> **Proof**: If you follow the instructions, the right-hand column shows that you always get the answer 1. **QED**

2   Think of a number, double it, subtract 4, multiply the result by 3, divide by 2, add 6, divide by 3. Prove that the answer will always equal the number you started with.

Elevens

Instructions	Numerical example	Algebraic generalisation
Write down any two digits.	5, 8	a, b
Form a two-digit number.	58	'ab' $= 10a + b$
Reverse the digits.	85	'ba' $= 10b + a$
Add the two numbers.	$58 + 85 = 143 = 11 \times 13$	$(10a + b) + (10b + a)$ $= 11(a + b)$

> **Claim**: No matter which two digits you start with, the right-hand column shows that the total will always be divisible by 11.

3 Prove that if you do the same thing with four digits (choose four digits, make a four-digit number, reverse and add) the total will always be divisible by 11.

4 What happens if you do the same with three digits?

Fibonacci

Instructions	Numerical example	Algebraic generalisation
Write down any two positive integers.	5, 11	a, b
Take these as the first two terms of a *Fibonacci-type* sequence, and write down the next three terms.	5	a
	11	b
	$16 (= 11 + 5)$	$b + a$
	$27 (= 16 + 11)$	$2b + a \, (= (b + a) + b)$
	$43 (= 27 + 16)$	$3b + 2a \, (= (2b + a)$ $+ (b + a))$

5 Is it true that, no matter which two numbers you start with,

    a the sum of the first and fifth terms will always be divisible by 3?

    b the sum of the first and ninth terms will always be divisible by 7?

    c the sum of the first and ninth terms will always be equal to 7 times the fifth term?

EXTRA 3

Greek cross

In this Greek cross, all twelve edges are of equal length. Draw a Greek cross on a piece of card and cut it out. Now divide the cross into four pieces with two straight cuts so that the pieces can be rearranged to make a square.

Solution: page 91

12 Telephone surveys

> This activity focuses on:
> • understanding mathematical text;
> • developing some of the statistical ideas associated with surveys.

Read the passage below. Then answer the questions that follow.

*In any survey the **sample** must be carefully chosen. In the 1936 Presidential elections in the USA there were two candidates – Landon and Roosevelt. On the whole, Landon represented relatively well-off voters and Roosevelt represented those who were less well-off.*

A magazine called Literary Digest conducted a postal survey asking which candidate people intended to vote for. They used a large sample, using names and addresses from telephone directories and car registration records. They assumed that this large sample would give an accurate prediction of the outcome of the election. Ten million people were sent questionnaires, and over two million replied. As a result the magazine predicted a massive victory for Landon. In the actual election, Roosevelt won a large majority!

*The problem with the survey was simple. In 1936, only 40% of Americans had telephones and only 55% had cars. So the sample was **biased**.*

Telephone surveys are now the most commonly used way of conducting surveys in America, and they are becoming more popular in Europe. A telephone survey has two surprising advantages.

- *People do not like ignoring the phone and simply letting it ring. The **median** number of rings before a phone is answered is four and over 90% of people answer before eight rings.*
- *There seems to be an unwritten rule that the person who starts a phone call is in control, and so is allowed to be the one who ends it.*

*Other advantages are speed and cost. A telephone survey costs about half as much as a similar face-to-face survey. The cost of a postal survey is about one fifth the cost of a telephone survey; but postal surveys take much longer, and the **response rates** can be very low.*

*Telephone interviewers follow a script. They usually work from a large office which contains between 20 and 100 sound-proof cubicles, each with a telephone. The interviewers usually spend between 10 and 20 minutes with each **subject**. They work four-hour shifts. There is normally a supervisor to check that the script is being followed and that the subjects are being treated correctly. Sometimes the script is displayed on a computer screen and the results are keyed in directly to the computer.*

*In any survey the selection of the sample is important. For many surveys the subjects are **chosen at random** from the local population. In the case of telephone surveys the sample may be chosen at random from a telephone directory stored on a computer. Lists of people in particular social categories can be purchased for more specialised surveys: for instance, a survey concerning nurses would be conducted using a **random sample** from a list of nurses in the required region.*

1 Write out in your own words the precise meaning of the words in bold type in the above passage.

2 Why did the 1936 *Literary Digest* survey result in a biased sample?

3 What was the response rate (as a percentage) for the *Literary Digest* survey?

4 How much more expensive are face-to-face surveys than postal surveys?

5 This table gives the number of separate telephone calls that were needed to contact people for one particular telephone survey:

Number of calls	1	2	3	4	5	6	7 or more
Number of people contacted	21 555	4374	2207	1230	1948	428	223

What do these figures suggest about the ease, or difficulty, of contacting a subject once he or she has been chosen as part of a sample in a telephone survey?

6   A lot of newspapers, and TV and radio stations conduct very simple 'opinion polls' called telephone polls, or phone-ins. These often address a single issue, such as 'Do you think this film should be banned?' People are invited to phone one number if they agree, and another if they do not. How unbiased do you think such a sample would be?

7   One criticism of telephone surveys is that they miss out the very poor and the very rich. Why do you think this might happen? How much would you expect this to affect the reliability of a telephone survey?

8   In what ways is a low response rate likely to lead to a biased sample?

9   a Why is it important for telephone interviewers to follow a script?

   b Do you think face-to-face interviewers should follow a script? Why?

EXTRA 4

Make a triangle

a   You have five sticks of lengths 1 cm, 2 cm, 3 cm, 4 cm, 5 cm. You have to choose three of these sticks which fit together to form the three sides of a triangle. How many different choices of three sticks are there which work?

b   What if you had ten sticks of lengths 1 cm to 10 cm?

Solution: page 91

13 *Probably right, but* …

This activity focuses on:

- developing simple ideas in probability;
- thinking carefully about mathematical arguments.

Organisation/Before you start:

- If you are working with a partner, divide the questions up so that each of you thinks about different questions. Then discuss and agree your final answers.

Below are six questions to explore.
At the end are six 'answers': **each answer may be right or wrong!**

First read a question and work out your own answer without looking at the answer given at the end of the section.

Then read the answer at the end of the section.
Think about your answer and the answer given at the end, and decide whether

- both are wrong, or
- both are right, or
- one is right and the other wrong.

In each case give a clear written reason to explain your final decision.
Then look up the solutions to see whether you were right.

1   A coin is tossed twice. What is the probability that a head will appear at least once?

2   Mr Patel has two children. You are told that at least one of them is a boy. What is the probability that both Mr Patel's children are boys?

3   Three coins are tossed together. What is the probability that they all come down the same – all heads or all tails?

4   Ben is playing a dice game with a normal, six-sided dice. If he throws a prime number or an even number, he scores a point. What is the probability that he scores a point on his next throw?

5   There are three counters in a bag: one counter has a cross on both sides, one has a circle on both sides, and one has a cross on one side and a circle on the other side. A counter is taken from the bag and laid on the table showing a cross. What is the probability that the other side also shows a cross?

6 Many games involve throwing two six-sided dice and adding the two numbers to give a total score. Usually the faces of the two dice are labelled 1, 2, 3, 4, 5, 6. Suppose that instead one dice has faces labelled 1, 3, 4, 5, 6, 8 and the other has faces labelled 1, 2, 2, 3, 3, 4. Will these two dice give the same set of possible totals?

Will they give the same probability for each total?

'Answer' 1

You can get a head on the first throw, a head on the second throw, or no heads at all. So a head occurs two out of three times; the probability is $\frac{2}{3}$.

'Answer' 2

We already know that one is a boy. The probability that the other is a boy is one half. So the probability that both children are boys is $\frac{1}{2}$.

'Answer' 3

There are three coins and only two possibilities (Heads or Tails) so at least two coins must come down the same. There is an even chance of the third coin showing a Head or a Tail. So the probability that all three coins come down the same is $\frac{1}{2}$.

'Answer' 4

There are six possible outcomes altogether. Three of them are even, and three of them are prime. So the probability that he scores a point is $\frac{6}{6}$ – he is bound to win!

'Answer' 5

The other side may have either a cross or a circle, so the probability is $\frac{1}{2}$.

'Answer' 6

If you number the two dice in such a crazy way, there is no way the totals and the probabilities could possibly be the same.

14 Magic squares

This activity focuses on:

- understanding mathematical text;
- following mathematical instructions;
- investigating magic squares.

Read the passage below and answer the questions that follow.

*A **magic square** contains consecutive positive integers, starting from 1, in a square array so that each row, each column and each of the two main diagonals has the same sum. This sum is called the **magic constant**.*

*The **order** of a magic square is the number of rows (or the number of columns). A magic square of order 1 is a square with 1 row (and 1 column) containing the number 1 by itself. There is no magic square of order 2.*

There is one basic magic square of order 3. All other magic squares of order 3 are obtained by rotating this one about its centre, or by reflecting it in one of the four dotted mirror lines.

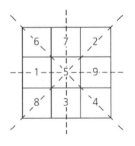

There are 880 different magic squares of order 4 (excluding rotations and reflections). The complete list was found in 1693. However, magic squares had been studied as long ago as 400 BC in China. In 1275 the Chinese mathematician Yang Hui gave a simple rule for constructing magic squares of order 4:

> *Place the numbers 1 to 16 in order in an array of four rows and four columns. Then exchange the numbers in opposite corners of the outer 4 by 4 square, and exchange the numbers in opposite corners of the inner 2 by 2 square. The result will be a magic square of order 4.*

In the seventeenth century the French ambassador to Siam learned of a way to make magic squares of any odd order ≥ 5. This Siamese method is illustrated here to construct a magic square of order 5.

> *Enter the integers in order, starting by putting 1 in the middle of an edge and moving diagonally up and to the right. When you hit the top row, start again in the bottom row – but one square to the right. When you hit the right-hand column, start again in the left-hand*

		3		
	2			
1				
7				5
			4	6

*column, but one square further up. If progress following these rules
is blocked, drop to the square just below the last one filled and
carry on from there.*

1 Why is there no magic square of order 2?

2 **a** Rotate and reflect the magic square of order 3 given in the text.
Check that the resulting squares are magic.

  b How many different magic squares of order 3 can be made by
rotating and reflecting the magic square given in the text?

3 An **anti-magic** square is one where the sums of the numbers in
each row, in each column, and in each of the two main diagonals
are all different. Construct an anti-magic square of order 3.

4 Use Yang Hui's method to change the square given here into a
magic square of order 4.
Check that the row totals, the column totals and the diagonal
totals are all the same.

1	2	3	4
5	6	7	8
9	10	11	12
13	14	15	16

5 Here is a magic square of order 4 with some interesting hidden
properties.

  a Add the squares of the numbers in the top two rows; then add
the squares of the numbers in the bottom two rows.

16	3	2	13
5	10	11	8
9	6	7	12
4	15	14	1

  b Add the squares of the numbers in the two diagonals; then add
the squares of the numbers not on a diagonal.

6 **a** Use the Siamese method to complete the magic square of order
5 given in the text. Check the row, column and diagonal totals.
What is the magic constant?

  b Use the method to construct a magic square of order 7.

7 **a** What is the magic constant for a magic square of order 3?
What is the magic constant for a magic square of order 4?
What is the magic constant for a magic square of order 5?

  b Numbers in the sequence $1, 1 + 2, 1 + 2 + 3, 1 + 2 + 3 + 4,$
$\ldots$ are called **triangular numbers**. There is a useful formula
for the nth triangular number:
$$1 + 2 + 3 + 4 + \ldots + n = \tfrac{1}{2}n(n + 1).$$
Use this formula to prove that the magic constant for any
magic square of order n is equal to $\tfrac{1}{2}n(n^2 + 1)$.

8 Here is one way to prove that that there is only one basic magic square of order 3.

   a First prove that the magic constant for any magic square of order 3 has to equal 15.

   b Then prove that the number in the central square of a magic square of order 3 has to be 5.

   c Check that the number 9 combines with exactly two other pairs of integers to make a total of 15. Conclude that 9 cannot go in a corner square.

   d Use this to show that there is essentially only one way of completing a magic square of order 3.

9 Here is a **magic hexagon** of order 3.
It is the only magic hexagon of any order.
In what way is it magic?

EXTRA 5

How many pieces?

Draw an isosceles right-angled triangle on thin paper, and cut it out.

   a Fold the triangle along its line of symmetry, and then fold it again along the line of symmetry of the folded triangle. **Imagine** cutting the twice-folded triangle along its line of symmetry. How many separate pieces of paper would you get?

   b Now imagine folding the original isosceles right-angled triangle N times before cutting the folded triangle along its line of symmetry. How many separate pieces of paper would you get?

Solution: page 91

Magic squares

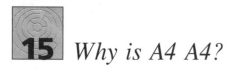

15 | *Why is A4 A4?*

In these activities the **length** of a rectangle is taken to mean the longer
side; the **width** is the shorter side.

Rectangles

1 • Make a sketch of a rectangle with width more than half the
    length.
    Estimate values for the length and for the width of your
    rectangle and write them on your sketch.

  • Halve your rectangle to get a second rectangle whose length is
    equal to the width of your previous rectangle, and whose width
    is equal to half the length of your previous rectangle.
    Make a sketch of your second rectangle and write these
    dimensions on your sketch.

  • Halve your second rectangle to obtain a third rectangle, whose
    length is equal to the width of your second rectangle, and
    whose width is equal to half the length of your second
    rectangle.
    Write these dimensions on a sketch of your third rectangle.

  • Repeat once more.

  • You now have four rectangles. For each rectangle, divide its
    length by its width. Write down what you notice.

2 Repeat question **1** starting with a different sized rectangle. Does
    the same thing happen when you work out the four quotients
    (length ÷ width)?

3 Can you find a starting rectangle for which all four quotients
    are equal?

A4, A5, A6

4 • Take a sheet of A4 paper and place it on the table.

- Take another sheet of A4, fold it exactly in half and cut it to make two **identical** A5 size sheets.
  Take one of the A5 sheets and place it next to the original A4 sheet.

- Take the other A5 sheet, fold it exactly in half and cut it to make two **identical** A6 size sheets.
  Take one of the two A6 sheets and place it next to the A4 sheet and the A5 sheet on the table.

- Compare the three sheets. Using your eyes, your ruler and your calculator find out as much as you can about each rectangle and about any relationships between the rectangles.

5 **a** Measure the length and width of the three sheets in question **4** as accurately as you can.

   b For each rectangle, divide the length by the width. What do you notice?

   c Calculate the square root of 2. How close is this to the result of each division in part **b**?

   d Use your measurements in part **a** to calculate the approximate dimensions of A3, A2, A1 and A0 size paper.

   e Hence calculate the approximate area of sheet of A0 size paper. What do you notice?

6 The size of A0 paper obeys two rules:

   i the area of an A0 sheet is 1 square metre;

   ii the ratio (length ÷ width) of an A0 sheet is equal to $\sqrt{2}$.

   Use this to calculate the dimensions of a sheet of A0 paper.

Triangles

7 - Take a sheet of A4 paper. Find out how to fold it so that you can cut off the largest possible square.

   - Fold the square along a diagonal, and carefully cut along the diagonal to produce two identical triangles. What can you say about the shape of these two triangles?

   - Take one of these triangles. Make a note of its properties and dimensions.

- Take the other triangle, fold it exactly in half and cut along the fold line to produce two smaller triangles. What do you know about the shape of these two smaller triangles?

- Place one of the small triangles on the table alongside the larger triangle.
  Fold the other small triangle and cut it into two identical triangles. Place one of these alongside the other two triangles.

- Compare the three triangles. Using your eyes, your ruler and your calculator find out as much as you can about each triangle and about any relationships between the triangles.

8 What is the size of the largest square that can be cut from an A0 sheet of paper? What is the length of the diagonal of this largest square?

9 a Measure as accurately as you can the lengths of the hypotentuse and of the shorter sides for each of the three triangles in question **7**.

b For each triangle, divide the length of the hypotenuse by the length of the shorter side. What do you notice?

c Calculate the square root of 2. How close is this to the result of each division in part **b**?

d Let $h < h' < h''$ be the lengths of the hypotenuses of the three triangles. Calculate $h'' \div h'$ and $h' \div h$. What do you notice?

Rectangle minus square equals ... ?

10 When you cut off the largest possible square from an A4 sheet, you are left with a long thin rectangle. Find out as much as you can about this rectangle.

EXTRA 6

Counting cells

Each cell in the human body contains about 2 metres of DNA. If all the DNA in all the cells of the human body was stretched end-to-end it would reach to the moon and back eight thousand times over. Roughly how many cells does this suggest there are in a single human body?

Solution: page 91

16 *Rules for number sequences*

This activity focuses on:

• finding a rule, and an expression for the *n*th term of a given number sequence;
• finding the *n*th term of a given counting sequence, and proving that it is correct.

Organisation/Before you start:

• If you are working with a partner, start by tackling questions **1–3** individually. Then compare and discuss your answers.

Number sequences

1 Bob and Diana both have sequences that begin 3, 6, ...
Bob says: The next numbers in my sequence are 12, 24, 48, ...
You just double each time.
Diana says: 'My sequence starts 3, 6, but the next numbers are 12, 21, 33, ...'

a What rule do you think Diana is using?

b Think of other ways to continue a sequence that begins
3, 6, ... Each time write down the next three terms and
describe the rule you are using.

2 Another sequence starts 2, 4, 6, 10, 16, 26, 42, ... Explain how
you think this sequence is generated and write down the next
three terms.

3 For each of the following sequences find a simple rule to generate
the sequence. Describe your rule in words. Then use it to write
down the next three terms.

a 3, 6, 9, 3, 6, 9, ...   **b** 3, 6, 9, 12, 15, 18, ...

c 3, 6, 9, 6, 9, 12, ...   **d** 3, 6, 9, 18, 21, 42, ...

e 3, 6, 9, 13, 17, 22, ...   **f** 3, 6, 9, 14, 19, 26, ...

g 3, 6, 9, 13, 17, 21, ...   **h** 3, 6, 9, 15, 21, 30, ...

i 3, 6, 9, 15, 24, 39, ...

Counting sequences from pictures

4 You can use unit squares to make a sequence of staircases. The first three staircases are shown on the right.

1 square 3 squares 6 squares

    a How many squares will there be in the next staircase?

    b How many squares will there be in the *n*th staircase? Give your answer in words and in symbols. Explain why it is correct.

5 Each of these questions shows the first three terms of a **sequence of diagrams**. In each question you have to find and **prove** a formula for the number of small shaded squares in the *n*th diagram.

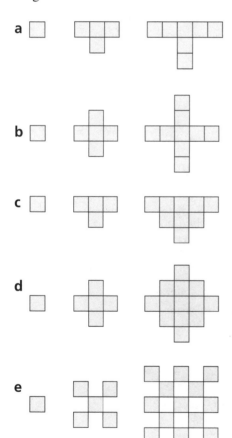

17 *Area*

This activity focuses on:

• extending knowledge and understanding of area;
• using area to explore some unusual problems.

These problems can be tackled in any order.

1 **a** In a kite one diagonal is a line of symmetry; so the two
diagonals are perpendicular.
If the diagonals have lengths a and b, calculate the area of the
kite in terms of a and b.

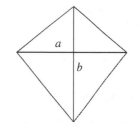

b Draw a quadrilateral whose diagonals are perpendicular to each
other, but which is not a kite.
If the two diagonals have lengths a and b, calculate the area of
the quadrilateral in terms of a and b.

2 Each side of a rectangle has length an integer number of
centimetres. The perimeter P cm and the area A cm^2 satisfy
$A = 3P$. How many different possible sizes are there for the
rectangle?

3 An arrowhead is drawn in a circle of radius r.
The distance between the points of the two tails is also equal to r.
Find the area of the arrowhead.

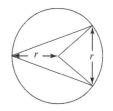

4 **a** Of all possible rectangles with perimeter 24 units, find the
dimensions of the rectangle with the largest possible area.

b Of all possible triangles with perimeter 24 units, which triangle
has the largest area?

c A story is told of how Queen Dido landed on the shores of
North Africa and was offered as much land as she could
enclose with the hide of an ox. She cut the ox-hide into a very
long thin strip and, using the straight seashore as one edge,
enclosed the largest possible area. On this land she founded the
ancient city of Carthage. What shape was the area of land that
she enclosed?

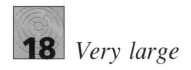

18 *Very large*

This activity focuses on:

- using standard index form and calculators to solve problems involving very large numbers;
- making mathematical sense of complex information.

You will need:

- a scientific calculator.

Read each section carefully. Then tackle the problems at the end.

Proxima Centauri

The diameter of the Earth is approximately 12 735 kilometres.
The diameter of the Sun is approximately 1 392 000 kilometres.
The Sun is the nearest star to the Earth and is about 150 million kilometres from the Earth. Light from the Sun takes about 500 seconds to reach the Earth.
The next nearest star to Earth is Proxima Centauri. Light from Proxima Centauri takes about 4.24 years to reach the Earth.

1 Suppose you build a model with the Sun as an orange.

   a How big should you make your model of the Earth?

   b How far away from the Sun should you position your model of the Earth?

   c How far away from the Sun should you position Proxima Centauri?

Krill

Krill are phosphorescent, planktonic shrimps. They occur in immense shoals around Antarctica, and are one of the most important organisms in the economy of Antarctic marine life. Krill are approximately 5 cm long. The total number of krill alive is estimated to be six hundred million million, and their total weight is about 650 million tonnes. It is estimated that when the whale population was at its height, whales ate 150 million tonnes of krill each year.
The weight of fish caught by human beings each year is around 70 million tonnes. There are about six billion people in the world.
A typical human being is between 1m and 2m tall and weighs between 40 kg and 100 kg.

2   Is the total weight of krill greater than or less than the total weight of human beings?

3   If human beings and krill each lined up end to end, which would be longer?

4   Which other interesting comparisons – involving whales, human beings and krill – can you deduce from the information given, or find out for yourself?

Calculator numbers

5   Enter 6 in your calculator display. Calculate the square of this number by pressing the $\boxed{x^2}$ key. Write down the answer.
Repeat the process of squaring and writing down the answer until the answer is bigger than 10^{12}.
Keep on squaring until the calculator gives up. Describe what happens when the answers get too big for the display.

6   What is the largest power of 6 that your calculator will accept?

7   **a** What is the biggest number you can show in your calculator display?

    b What is the square of the number in part **a**?

A moment of eternity

Alpha: *I heard a legend which described a **Moment of Eternity**. It said there is a mountain 16 km wide and 16 km high. Once in every thousand years a bird visits the mountain and sharpens its beak on the rock of that mountain, wearing away a tiny piece of rock each time. When the mountain has been completely worn away, a single Moment of Eternity will have passed.*

Beta: *So how long is a Moment of Eternity according to this story?*

Alpha: *Well first we need to work out how big the mountain is.*

Beta: *Mountains are roughly cone shaped. Let's look up how to calculate the volume of a cone.*

Alpha: *It is $\frac{1}{3}\pi r^2 h$, where r is the radius of the base and h is the height.*

Beta: *Then $r = 8$ km, so the volume is $\frac{1}{3} \times \pi \times 8^2 \times 16$ cubic kilometres!*

Very large   41

Alpha: *That's a little over 1000 cubic kilometres. Since we are estimating, we can forget the extra and take the volume to be 1000 cubic kilometres.*

Beta: *How much do you think the bird would wear away each time?*

Alpha: *It must be tiny. Shall we guess about 1 cubic millimetre?*

8 Calculate the exact volume of a cone of height 16 km and with a circular base of diameter 16 km.

9 Estimate how many years it would take for the bird to make the mountain disappear.

10 How does this length of time compare with the total age of the universe (which astronomers estimate to be around 10 billion years old)?

11 Suppose the bird began its visits at the beginning of the universe, and finally wore away the mountain in the year 2000AD. How often (for example, how many times each year, or each century) would the bird have had to visit the mountain to sharpen its beak?

EXTRA 7

Days in the year

a Write 365, the number of days in the year, as the sum of consecutive squares in two different ways.

b Is it possible to write 366, the number of days in a leap year, in a similar way?

Solution: page 92

19 *Three coins in a line*

This activity focuses on:

• exploring and using an unfamiliar algebraic notation.

Organisation/Before you start:

• You will need three coins.

Read the following instructions. Then answer questions **1–4**.

• Place three coins in a line, all showing heads.   (H)   (H)   (H)

• You are allowed to make three kinds of moves: *L*, *R*, and *S*.
  Move *L* means 'turn over the left two coins',
      so **H H H** changes to **T T H**.
  Move *R* means 'turn over the right two coins',
      so **H H H** changes to **H T T**.
  Move *S* means 'turn over the two outer coins',
      so **H H H** changes to **T H T**.

• You can combine moves by doing one move after another; we
  denote this by *.

  So *L*R* means 'do *L* followed by *R*':

  $\left. \begin{array}{l} L \text{ changes } \mathbf{H\,H\,H} \text{ to } \mathbf{T\,T\,H} \\ \text{and } R \text{ then changes } \mathbf{T\,T\,H} \text{ to } \mathbf{T\,H\,T} \end{array} \right\}$ so *L*R* changes **H H H** to **T H T**.

Therefore *L*R* has the same effect as *S*; so *L*R* = *S*.

1 a Find another name for the combined move *S*R*.

   b Find another name for the combined move *S*L*.

2 a Find another name for the combined move *R*L*.

   b What is the connection between *R*L* and *L*R*?.

3 a Find another name for *R*L*R*.

   b Find another name for *L*R*L*.

4 a Find another name for *R*R*.

   b Find another name for *L*L*.

In question **4** you need a name for the move that leaves the coins
unchanged! Write this move as *I*, and call it the **identity** move (or the
do nothing move).

You can now make a table of combinations for the four moves **R**, **L**, **S**, **I**; in the row labelled by **L** and the column labelled by **R**, enter the name of the combined move **L∗R**: **L∗R = S**.

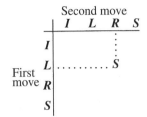

5   Copy and complete the table of combinations.

6   Just as in simple algebra, write **R∗R∗R** as R^3.
    Work out the single names for the following combined moves.

   a R^3 b R^5 c R^6 d R^{500}
   e S^3 f S^4 g S^{33} h S^{500}

7   **L**, **R**, **S** and **I** are four ways of turning over some (or none) of the coins.

   a How many other ways are there of turning over some, or all (or none) of the three coins?

   b Starting from **H H H** is it possible to end up with **T T T** if you are only allowed to use the moves **L**, **R**, and **S**?

EXTRA 8

Symmetrical years

1961 is a 'symmetrical date', since it is unchanged by a half turn. What is the next year after 1961 with this property? Which other years are like this?

Solution: page 92

20 *Three by three revisited*

This activity focuses on:

- exercising spatial sense in 2-dimensions;
- systematic enumeration.

Organisation/Before you start:

- You will need squared paper.

All the activities in this section refer to the 3 by 3 grid on the right.

- Choose one of the tasks **A–E** and solve the problem.
- Then develop and extend the task by asking related 'What if ...?' questions of your own.

A **a** You may remove one small square from the 3 by 3 grid. How many different (that is, non-congruent) shapes could you make?

b What if you are allowed to remove **two** small squares?

B The 3 by 3 square could be made by fitting **nine** 1 by 1 squares together; it could also be made by fitting **six** squares together – one 2×2 and five 1×1s.

a How many different ways are there of fitting smaller squares together to make a 4 by 4 square?

b How many different ways are there of fitting smaller rectangles together to make a 3 by 3 square?

C Place a black chess knight, or rook, on each of the two top corner squares of the 3 by 3 square, and a white knight on each of the bottom two corner squares. The knights move as in chess, and can only move onto an empty square. Is it possible for the black and white knights to exchange places? If so, what is the smallest number of moves needed?

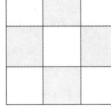

D By cutting along grid lines you can cut the 3 by 3 square into two non-congruent pieces: for example, a 3 by 1 rectangle and a 3 by 2 rectangle. What is the largest number of possible pieces you can get if no two of the pieces are allowed to be congruent?

E If you colour all squares in the 3 by 3 square the same colour, the resulting pattern has rotational symmetry of order 4, and four lines of reflection symmetry. Which of the other combinations in the table can be achieved by patterns of coloured squares?

		Number of lines of symmetry				
		0	1	2	3	4
Order of rotational symmetry	1	·	·	·	·	·
	2	·	·	·	·	·
	3	·	·	·	·	·
	4	·	·	·	·	✓

21 *Puzzles*

1 How many right angles?

In a triangle you can have at most one right angle. In a quadrilateral you can have four right angles. What is the largest number of (internal) right angles you can have in a decagon?

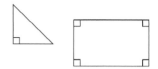

2 Consecutive sums

a Take three consecutive integers, and add them. Is their sum divisible by 3? Is it always true that the sum of three consecutive integers is divisible by 3? If it is, explain why; if it is not, give an example.

b What can you say (and prove!) about the sum of any **five** consecutive integers?

c What can you say (and prove!) about the sum of any **four** consecutive integers?

3 Baseball caps

This baseball cap has 6 panels and 1 peak. The material for each part can be either of two colours. How many different colour combinations are possible?

4 Where's the centre?

Draw round a circular object to produce a circle, but with its centre unmarked.

a Find a way to locate the approximate centre by folding.

b Suppose you are not allowed to fold. Can you locate the exact centre using only a straight edge and a pair of compasses?

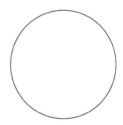

5 Mystery train

Some time ago Mike regularly took the train from Chichester to Victoria. There were two trains each hour – one via Horsham and the other via Hove. He never bothered to consult the timetable but simply turned up randomly and took the first train that came. Yet he almost always landed up going via Horsham. Can you explain why?

6 Everest

If the Earth were the size of a football, would you be able to feel Mount Everest with your fingers?

7 Piles of money

I am making two piles of pound coins by choosing a pile at random with probability $\frac{1}{2}$, and then adding a coin to that pile. At the moment Pile A has two pound coins and Pile B has three pound coins. What is the probability that Pile A will be the first to have five pound coins?

8 Wrap up the Earth

Imagine a single loop of wire wrapped around the Equator at sea level, and another loop, also round the Equator, but one metre above sea level all the way round. How much longer is the second loop than the first loop?

Puzzles

47

CHALLENGES

Does it go? How do you know?

1 **a** An integer is exactly divisible by 100 when its tens and units digits are both zero.
   Proof: 100, 1000, 10 000, etc. are all divisible by 100.
   A number like 12 345, stands for

$$1\times(10\,000) + 2\times(1000) + 3\times100 + 4\times10 + 5.$$

   The first three terms are all divisible by 100;

   ∴ the remainder when you divide 12 345 by 100

   is the same as

   the remainder when you divide $4\times10 + 5$ by 100.

   So the original number is divisible by 100 only if its tens and units digits are both zero. **QED**

   b An integer is exactly divisible by 1000 when its hundreds, tens and units digits are all zero.
   Proof: 1000, 10 000, 100 000, etc. are all divisible by 1000.
   A number like 123 456 stands for

$$1\times(100\,000) + 2\times(10\,000) + 3\times1000 + 4\times100 + 5\times10 + 6.$$

   The first three terms are all divisible by 1000;
   So the remainder when you divide 123 456 by 1000 is the same as the remainder when you divide $4\times100 + 5\times10 + 6 = 456$ by 1000. **QED**

2 **a** An integer is exactly divisible by 5 when its units digit is divisible by 5 – that is, when its units digit is 0 or 5.
   Proof: 10, 100, 1000, etc. are all divisible by 10, and so also by 5.
   A number like 1234 stands for

$$1\times(1000) + 2\times(100) + 3\times10 + 4.$$

   The first three terms are all divisible by 5;
   ∴ the remainder when you divide any number (such as 1234) by 5 is equal to the remainder when you divide the units digit by 5 (in this case 4). **QED**

   b An integer is exactly divisible by 25 when the number formed by its tens and units digits is divisible by 25 – that is, when the last two digits are 00, 25, 50, or 75.
   Proof: 100, 1000, 10 000, etc. are all divisible by 100, and so are also divisible by 25. **QED**

3 a An integer is exactly divisible by 2 when its units digit is divisible by 2 – that is, when its units digit is even (0, 2, 4, 6, or 8).
Proof: 10, 100, 1000, etc. are all divisible by 10, and so are also divisible by 2. **QED**

b An integer is exactly divisible by 4 when the number formed by its tens and units digits is divisible by 4.
Proof: 100, 1000, 10 000, etc. are all divisible by 100, and so are also divisible by 4. **QED**

c An integer is exactly divisible by 8 when the number formed by its hundreds, tens and units digits is divisible by 8.
Proof: 1000, 10 000, 100 000, etc. are all divisible by 1000, and so are also divisible by 8. **QED**

4 a 123 456: $1 + 2 + 3 + 4 + 5 + 6 = 21 = 2\times9 + 3$;
$\therefore$ remainder $= 3$.

b 1 234 567: $1 + 2 + 3 + 4 + 5 + 6 + 7 = 28 = 3\times9 + 1$;
$\therefore$ remainder $= 1$.

c 12 345 678: $1 + 2 + 3 + 4 + 5 + 6 + 7 + 8 = 36 = 4\times9$;
$\therefore$ remainder $= 0$.

d 123 456 789: $1 + 2 + 3 + 4 + 5 + 6 + 7 + 8 + 9 = 45 = 5\times9$;
$\therefore$ remainder $= 0$.

5 a Divisibility by 3
$$1234 = 1\times1000 + 2\times100 + 3\times10 + 4$$
$$= 1(999 + 1) + 2(99 + 1) + 3(9 + 1) + 4$$
$$= (1\times999 + 2\times99 + 3\times9) + (1 + 2 + 3 + 4)$$
$$= \text{(multiple of 3)} + \text{(sum of digits)}.$$
So when you divide 1234 by 3, the remainder is the same as when you divide the digit sum $1 + 2 + 3 + 4 = 10$ by 3: remainder $= 1$.

b 123 has digit sum $1 + 2 + 3 = 6$, so remainder $= 0$: 123 is divisible by 3.
1234 has digit sum $1 + 2 + 3 + 4 = 10$, so remainder $= 1$.
12 345 has digit sum 15, so remainder $= 0$: 12 345 is divisible by 3.
123 456 has digit sum 21, so remainder $= 0$: 123 456 is divisible by 3.
1 234 567 has digit sum 28, so remainder $= 1$.

Does it go? How do you know?

COMMENTS & SOLUTIONS

Divisibility by 6

An integer is exactly divisible by 6 when it is divisible by both 2 and 3. So the final digit must be even, and the digit sum must be divisible by 3. Only 123 456 has both properties.

6 See *The Penguin dictionary of curious and interesting numbers* by David Wells (Penguin 1997), pages 51, 63.

2 *True, False and 'Iffy' shape statements*

Definitely true: A, I, J, M, P

A A **rectangle** is a quadrilateral with four right angles; so every square is a rectangle.

I This is not obvious. (Start with one copy of your chosen quadrilateral Q and rotate it through a half turn about the midpoint of each side to get the four neighbours of Q. Keep going.)

J This simple fact is so useful it has a name: **the triangle inequality**.

M A rhombus is a special parallelogram (with all four sides equal).

P If the perpendicular from A meets DC between D and C, cut off the triangle ADX and fit AD along BC as shown.

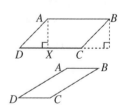

If X does not lie between D and C, cut instead along the perpendicular from A to BC.

Definitely false: B, E, H, K

B Obtuse angles are greater than $90°$, so two of them would add to more than $180°$.

E When you double the sides of a square the area is multiplied by $2^2 = 4$.

H When you double the radius of a circle the area is multiplied by $2^2 = 4$.

COMMENTS & SOLUTIONS

K A 1 cm by 24 cm rectangle has area 24 cm² and perimeter 50 cm; a 2 cm by 12 cm rectangle has area 24 cm² and perimeter 28 cm.

Two rectangles with the same area have equal perimeters only if they are congruent.

'Iffy' : C, D, F, G, L, N, O

> Each **'Iffy'** statement has been made more precise by adding some underlined words to the original statement.

There are many different ways of making each **'Iffy'** statement precise. We give the most obvious correct version.
If your answer is not the same as the answer given here, you will have to decide whether your answer is correct.

C The diagonals of a rectangle cross at right angles <u>only if the rectangle is a square.</u>

D If A is 20 cm from B, and B is 10 cm from C, then A is 30 cm from C <u>only if A, B and C lie on a straight line with B between A and C.</u>

F A parallelogram has rotation symmetry of order 4 <u>only if it is a square.</u>

G A parallelogram is a rectangle <u>only if one of its angles is 90°.</u>

L Cutting a kite along a diagonal <u>which is a line of symmetry</u> produces two congruent triangles.

N Four straight lines cross at six different points <u>if and only if no two of the lines are parallel, and no three lines pass through a single point.</u>

O If two lines <u>lie in the same plane and</u> are perpendicular to a third line, they must be parallel to each other.

In the cube shown here, the lines AC and BD are both perpendicular to the edge AB, but are not parallel.

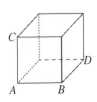

3 Counting back in time

1 **Chinese:** Based on 10; $10 + x$ has the prefix **shih-** in front of the word for x.
$10 \times x$ has the suffix **-shih** at the end of the word for x.
10 000 has a special word *wan*, which is used systematically.

Aztec: Based on a mixture of 5 and 10. What do you notice about 15 and 30?

Traditional Welsh: Starts off based on 10; but sixteen, seventeen and nineteen link to fifteen. The decades are linked to twenty. Modern Welsh is strictly based on ten, but traditional number names are often used in everyday speech.

3 Couple, duo, double, twins, ...

4 Score. The apparently different meanings all have a common root.

5 **a** 123   **b** ⌇99∩∩∩||||

6 **a** In 1492 Columbus discovered America.

b In 1776 America discovered itself (by declaring independence from Britain).

7 IC, LXLIX, LIL, and others.

8 One million million million, two hundred and thirty four thousand five hundred and sixty seven million million, eight hundred and ninety thousand nine hundred and eighty seven million, six hundred and fifty four thousand three hundred and twenty one.
(Or, using **Section 5: BIG names**, one quintillion, two hundred and thirty four quadrillion, five hundred and sixty seven trillion, eight hundred and ninety billion, nine hundred and eighty seven million, six hundred and fifty four thousand, three hundred and twenty one.)

4 Fractions bits and pieces

You may guess the answer to some of these problems by pattern-spotting from particular examples. But to prove that your guess is correct you have to use **algebra**. Try to understand the full algebraic solutions given here – you will need the ideas later. But don't worry if some bits seem rather hard.

1 **Example**: Suppose we start with $\frac{7}{10}$.
   Then we get this sequence of fractions:

$$\frac{7}{10} \to \frac{6}{9} \to \frac{5}{8} \to \frac{4}{7} \to \frac{3}{6} = \frac{1}{2}.$$

2 If you start with $\frac{7}{10}$ it takes 4 steps.
   The number of steps, 4, can be easily predicted as soon as you know the numerator $p = 7$, and the denominator $q = 10$: then the number of steps $2p - q = 2 \times 7 - 10 = 4$.

   Proof: Start with a fraction $\frac{p}{q}$ less than 1 and greater than $\frac{1}{2}$.

   Then $0 < \dfrac{p}{q} < 1$; $\therefore p < q$

   and $\dfrac{p}{q} > \dfrac{1}{2}$; $\therefore q < 2p.$

   After k steps the numerator and denominator have been reduced by k; $\therefore$ the new fraction $= \dfrac{p-k}{q-k}$.

   This new fraction equals $\frac{1}{2}$ precisely when $\frac{p-k}{q-k} = \frac{1}{2}$, that is
   $$2(p - k) = q - k. \quad (1)$$

   In any particular case we know the values of p and q, and we want to find k, so we solve the equation (1) to find k in terms of p and q. Add $2k - q$ to each side of (1) to get

   $$2p - 2k + (2k - q) = q - k + (2k - q)$$
   $$\therefore 2p - q = k. \quad \textbf{QED}$$

   When $p = 7$ and $q = 10$ as in the example from question **1**, this tells you that the number k of steps is given by $k = 2p - q = 4$.

Extension

   a Start with a fraction between $\frac{1}{3}$ and 1 and repeatedly subtract 1 from both the numerator and the denominator. Do you always get a fraction which is equivalent to $\frac{1}{3}$? How can you tell in advance whether you will get a fraction equivalent to $\frac{1}{3}$?

   b When do you eventually get a fraction equivalent to $\frac{1}{4}$?

3 The answer is 2.

Proof: The answer must be
slightly greater than $1 + \frac{1}{2}$, which is equal to $2 - \frac{1}{2}$;
and slightly greater than $1 + \frac{1}{2} + \frac{1}{4}$, which equals $2 - \frac{1}{4}$;
and slightly greater than $1 + \frac{1}{2} + \frac{1}{4} + \frac{1}{8}$, which equals $2 - \frac{1}{8}$;
and so on. **QED**

4 The answer is $\frac{2}{3}$.

Proof: **(1)** The first step is to show that $\frac{1}{4} + \frac{1}{16} + \frac{1}{64} + \ldots = \frac{1}{3}$.
Here's why. You can divide a cake between three people like
this:

- cut the cake into four quarters, and give $\frac{1}{4}$ to each person, leaving $\frac{1}{4}$;

- cut this spare $\frac{1}{4}$ into four equal parts, giving four $\frac{1}{16}$s; then give $\frac{1}{16}$ to each of the three people, leaving $\frac{1}{16}$;

- cut the remaining $\frac{1}{16}$ into four parts, and give each person $\frac{1}{64}$. If you keep on going like this forever, the cake will have been shared equally between three people, and each person will have received $\frac{1}{4} + \frac{1}{16} + \frac{1}{64} + \ldots = \frac{1}{3}$.

(2) The second step is to double this to get:
$\frac{1}{2} + \frac{1}{8} + \frac{1}{32} + \frac{1}{128} + \ldots = \frac{2}{3}$.

(3) Finally add 1 to the equation at the end of (1) and subtract the
equation in (2) to get:
$1 - \frac{1}{2} + \frac{1}{4} - \frac{1}{8} + \frac{1}{16} - \frac{1}{32} + \frac{1}{64} - \frac{1}{128} + \ldots = (1 + \frac{1}{3}) - \frac{2}{3} = \frac{2}{3}$. **QED**

5 **a** $\frac{7}{8} = \frac{1}{2} + \frac{1}{4} + \frac{1}{8}$

b $\frac{7}{12} = \frac{1}{2} + \frac{1}{12}$

c $\frac{10}{13} = \frac{1}{2} + \frac{1}{4} + \frac{1}{52}$

$\frac{7}{8} = \frac{1}{2} + \frac{1}{3} + \frac{1}{24}$; $\quad \frac{7}{12} = \frac{1}{3} + \frac{1}{4}$; $\quad \frac{10}{13} = \frac{1}{2} + \frac{1}{5} + \frac{1}{15} + \frac{1}{390}$;

6 Every proper fraction can be written as a sum of different unit
fractions.

- The method is clear. (To understand why it works, see the
proof below.)
If you start with $\frac{10}{13}$, take the biggest possible unit fraction –
namely $\frac{1}{2}$;
subtract this from $\frac{10}{13}$ to get the remainder $\frac{7}{26}$.
Next take the largest unit fraction less than $\frac{7}{26}$ – namely $\frac{1}{4}$;

subtract this from $\frac{7}{26}$ to get the remainder.
Keep going until the remainder is itself a unit fraction.

- **Proof that this always works**: Suppose the fraction you start with is $\frac{p}{q}$.
  Choose the unit fraction $\frac{1}{n} \leq \frac{p}{q}$ with the smallest possible denominator n;

  $\therefore \frac{1}{n}$ is the largest unit fraction $\leq \frac{p}{q}$.

  $\therefore \frac{1}{n} \leq \frac{p}{q} < \frac{1}{n-1}$.

  Notice that $\frac{p}{q} < \frac{1}{n-1}$ means that $p(n-1) < q$;

  $\therefore pn - q < p$. (1)

  When we subtract $\frac{1}{n}$ from $\frac{p}{q}$, the remainder will be
  $\frac{p}{q} - \frac{1}{n} = \frac{pn-q}{qn}$; but $pn - q < p$ (from (1)),
  so the numerator $pn - q$ of this remainder $\frac{pn-q}{qn}$ is smaller
  than the numerator p of the previous fraction $\frac{p}{q}$.
  At each step the numerator of the remainder gets smaller and smaller;
  $\therefore$ you must eventually get a remainder with numerator 1.

  QED

7 The easiest pair to find is 2, 2 (with $2 + 2 = 2 \times 2$).

The easiest family of pairs is probably

$$2, 1\tfrac{1}{1}; \quad 3, 1\tfrac{1}{2}; \quad 4, 1\tfrac{1}{3}; \quad 5, 1\tfrac{1}{4}; \ \ldots .$$

8 - Given any value of a (except for $a = 1$), choose $b = \frac{a}{a-1}$.
  Then a, b satisfy $a + b = a \times b$.
  Proof: $a + b = a + \dfrac{a}{a-1} = \dfrac{a(a-1) + a}{a-1} = \dfrac{a^2}{a-1}$;

  $$ab = a \cdot \frac{a}{a-1} = \frac{a^2}{a-1}. \quad \textbf{QED}$$

- These are the only pairs of numbers a, b which satisfy $a + b = a \times b$.

  Proof: Suppose two unknown numbers a and b have the property, $a + b = a \times b$.

  $$\therefore a = ab - b = b(a - 1)$$

Fractions bits and pieces   55

$$\therefore b = \frac{a}{a-1}. \quad \textbf{QED}$$

9, 10

$$\frac{1}{2}: \quad = \frac{1}{2}(\text{using } 1,2); \quad = \frac{215}{430}(\text{using } 0,1,2,3,4,5)$$

$$\frac{1}{3}: \quad = \frac{34}{102}(\text{using } 0,1,2,3,4)$$

$$\frac{1}{4}: \quad = \frac{3}{12}(\text{using } 1,2,3)$$

$$\frac{1}{5}: \quad = \frac{2}{10}(\text{using } 0,1,2)$$

$$\frac{1}{6}: \quad = \frac{2943}{17\,658}(\text{using } 1,2,3,4,5,6,7,8,9)$$

$$\frac{1}{7}: \quad = \frac{3}{21}(\text{using } 1,2,3)$$

$$\frac{1}{8}: \quad = \frac{3}{24}(\text{using } 2,3,4); \quad = \frac{4}{32}(\text{using } 2,3,4); \quad = \frac{7}{56}(\text{using } 5,6,7)$$

$$\frac{1}{9}: \quad = \frac{6}{54}(\text{using } 4,5,6).$$

5 BIG names

1 If a number in the new system has numerical value 10^n, the number with the same name in the old system has numerical value 10^{2n-6}.

2 In both systems, each number name has a **pre-fix** (bi-, tri-, etc.). Each of these prefixes itself stands for a number: bi- means 2; tri- means 3; etc.

  a In the old system, if the pre-fix of a number name stands for m, then the number represented by this name is 10^{6m}.

  b In the new system, if the pre-fix of a number name stands for m, then the number represented by this name is 10^{3m+3}.

3 The pre-fix **cent-** stands for 100.

  a So in the old system a centrillion would be equal to 10^{600}.

  b In the new system a centrillion would be equal to 10^{303}.

4 **Quad** stands for 4; **quint** stands for 5; **nono** stands for 9.

    a quadrillion $\times$ quintillion = nonillion

$$4\text{-illion} \times 5\text{-illion} = 9\text{-illion}$$

$$10^{4 \times 6} \times 10^{5 \times 6} = 10^{9 \times 6}.$$

In the old system, when you **multiply** numbers you **add** the pre-fixes! When you multiply a quadrillion by a quintillion, the answer is a nonillion: the number whose name has the pre-fix meaning $9(= 4 + 5)$.

    b The new system does not have quite such a nice property. Instead, to work out the name for the product of two numbers, you do the same as before **and then add one:**

quadrillion $\times$ quintillion = (nono + 1)illion = decillion

$$4\text{-illion} \times 5\text{-illion} = (4 + 5 + \mathbf{1})\text{-illion}.$$

In general

$$10^{3m+3} \times 10^{3p+3} = 10^{3(m+p+1)+3}.$$

5   **a** In the old system:

$$6\text{-illion} \times 7\text{-illion} = 13\text{-illion} = \text{tredecillion} = 10^{6 \times 13} = 10^{78}.$$

    b In the new system:

$$6\text{-illion} \times 7\text{-illion} = (6 + 7 + 1)\text{-illion}$$

$$= \text{quattuordecillion} = 10^{3 \times 14 + 3} = 10^{45}.$$

6   **a** A **gillion** is the old name for $10^9 = 1\,000\,000\,000$.

    b A **googol** is another name for 10^{100}.

    c A **googolplex** is another name for 10^{googol}.

Googol and **googolplex** were introduced in the popular book *Mathematics and the imagination* by E. Kasner and J. Newman (G. Bell and Sons, London 1949, pages 20–25). See also *The Penguin dictionary of curious and interesting numbers* by David Wells (Penguin 1997), pages 202–203.

7 Archimedes showed that the number of grains of sand in the universe (which he took to be a huge sphere – the sphere of the fixed stars – centred on the Sun, with radius much much larger than the distance from the Earth to the Sun) **could not be more than** 10^{51}. So $N = 10^{51}$.

See *The Penguin dictionary of curious and interesting numbers* by David Wells (Penguin 1997), pages 199–200.

6 *Quadrilaterals*

Questions **1–6a** encourage you to go and find things out, so no answers are provided.

6 b Here is one possible answer:

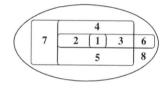

Region **1**: all squares
Regions **1** and **2**: all rectangles
Regions **1** and **3**: all rhombuses
Regions **1, 2, 3** and **4**: all parallelograms
Regions **1, 2, 3** and **5**: all trapezia
Regions **3** and **6**: all kites
Regions **1, 2, 3, 4, 5, 6** and **7**: all convex quadrilaterals
Region **8**: all non-convex quadrilaterals.

7 a It should look like a parallelogram.

b It again looks like a parallelogram.

c One way is to start with a ∗e∗∗a∗∗∗e, but this is not the only way. In general, to end with a rhombus you only need to start with a quadrilateral whose two diagonals are equal in length. You should be able to prove this once you have completed question **8**.

8 a The Midpoint Theorem: Given any triangle *ABC*, if *M* and *N* are the midpoints of the sides *AB* and *BC*, then *MN* is parallel to *AC*, and is half as long as *AC*.

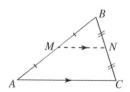

b Start with an unknown quadrilateral *ABCD*.
Mark the midpoints *M*, *N*, *P*, *Q* of the four sides *AB*, *BC*, *CD*, *DA*.

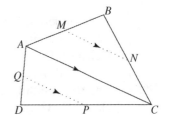

    i Construction: Draw the line segment *AC*.

    Now apply The Midpoint Theorem twice:

- first to the triangle *ABC*, to show that *MN* is parallel to, and half as long as, *AC*;

- then to the triangle *ADC*, to show that *QP* is parallel to, and half as long as, *AC*.

    So *MN* is parallel to *QP*, and $MN = QP \ (= \frac{1}{2}AC)$.

    ii Now rub out the line segment *AC*, and decide which construction line you should draw to show that *PN* is parallel to *QM*, and that *PN = QM*.

    Combining **i** and **ii** shows that *MNPQ* is always a parallelogram.

7 *Dozens of different ways of counting*

1 **a** 1, 2, 3, 4, 6, 12.

    b 1, 2, 5, 10.

2 **a** Smallest: $12 = 2^2 \times 3$. Next smallest: $20 = 2^2 \times 5$.

    b $64 = 2^6$.

3 **a** $48 (= 4 \times 12)$ **b** $120 (= 10 \times 12)$

    c $178 (= 1 \times 12^2 + 2 \times 12 + 10)$ **d** $143 (= 11 \times 12 + 11)$.

4 **a** $50 (= 5 \times 12)$ **b** $84 (= 8 \times 12 + 4)$

    c $180 (= 1 \times 12^2 + 8 \times 12)$ **d** $ED (= 11 \times 12 + 10)$.

5 **a** 12 inches = 1 foot; 3 feet = 1 yard; 220 yards = 1 furlong; 8 furlongs = 1 mile.

    b 16 ounces = 1 pound; 14 pounds = 1 stone; 8 stone = 1 hundredweight; 20 hundredweight = 1 ton.

    c The different systems of weights that have been used over the years (Ancient Greek, Roman, Arabic, Saxon, Avoirdupois,

Troy, Imperial, Metric) could be the subject of a long essay!
Troy was a city in ancient Greece – famous for the beautiful
Helen of Troy, and for being successfully invaded by troops
concealed inside a large wooden horse.

The **troy pound** was first mentioned in a 1414 statute of
Henry V, which dealt with the price and composition of English
goldsmiths' work in silver-gilt. The troy system was:
24 grains = 1 pennyweight; 20 pennyweight = 1 ounce;
12 ounces = 1 pound.

6 a The digits in positions other than the units digit all represent
multiples of 12, and 12 has 2 and 3 as a factor. So the crucial
thing is whether the units digit has 2 or 3 as a factor.

b As in part **a** it is enough to check whether the units digit has 4
as a factor. So a number written in base 12 has 4 as a factor
precisely when the units digit is 0, or 4, or 8.

c A number written in base 12 has 6 as a factor precisely when
its units digit is 0 or 6.

A number written in base 12 has 12 as a factor precisely when
its units digit is 0.

A number written in base 12 has 8 as a factor precisely when
its last two digits 'du' represent a number (base 12) which has
8 as a factor: that is, when either
• the dozens digit d is even and the units digit u is 0 or 8, or
• the dozens digit d is odd and the units digit u is 4.

A number written in base 12 has 9 as a factor precisely when
its last two digits 'du' represent a number which has 9 as a
factor: that is, when either
• d is a multiple of 3 and $u = 9$, or
• d is 1 more than a multiple of 3 and $u = 6$, or
• d is 2 more than a multiple of 3 and $u = 3$.

7 A **gross** is equal to a dozen dozens, or $144(= 12^2)$.

8 **Time:** 60 seconds = 1 minute; 60 minutes = 1 hour.
Angle: 60 seconds = 1 minute; 60 minutes = 1 degree.
        (But 1 full turn = 360 degrees!)

10 $1161(\text{base } 12) = 1 \times 12^3 + 1 \times 12^2 + 6 \times 12 + 1 = 1945 \text{ (base 10)}$.

11 You could ask your grandparents, or look in some old (pre-1970)
maths textbooks.

8   *True, False and 'Iffy' negative number statements*

It is important to learn to make precise, mathematically correct
statements.
To help show what is meant by a 'mathematically correct'
statement, these answers are very full – even though this may make
them a bit hard to read.

Definitely true : E, F   ⎱   If you disagree with any of these, think again.

Definitely false : A, J, N ⎰   If you remain unsure, ask your teacher.

'Iffy': B, C, D, G, H, I, K, L, M

Each **'Iffy'** statement has been made more precise by adding some
underlined words to the original statement.

There are many different ways of making each **'Iffy'** statement precise.
We give the most obvious correct version.
If your answer is not the same as the answer given here, you will have
to decide whether your answer is correct.

B   The sum of two numbers is greater than their difference <u>only if
the numbers are both positive</u>.

     Proof: Let the two numbers be x and y, with $x \geq y$.
     Suppose that their sum $x + y$ is greater than their difference $x - y$.

       $x + y > x - y$

     $\therefore \quad 2y > 0$

     $\therefore \quad\;\; y > 0$

     But $x \geq y$, so we must also have $x > 0$.   **QED**

C   <u>The product of</u> two negative <u>numbers is</u> a positive <u>number</u>.

     The shorter version may be easier to remember, but the operation
really matters!

D   If n is negative, then $\frac{1}{n}$ is less than $^{-}1$ <u>only if $^{-}1 < n < 0$</u>.

     Proof: Suppose that $\frac{1}{n} < {}^{-}1$.
     Since n is negative, multiplying both sides by n reverses the
inequality.

       $\therefore 1 > {}^{-}n$

       $\therefore n > {}^{-}1$.   **QED**

G If subtracting one negative number x from another negative number y gives a positive answer, <u>then the positive numbers ^-x, ^-y satisfy $^-x > {}^-y$.</u>

Note: To make the statement more precise, it is essential to give the two numbers **names:** x and y.
Notice that x and y here stand for **negative** numbers.

Proof: Suppose that $y - x > 0$.

Then $y > x$

$\therefore$ $^-x > {}^-y$. **QED**

H When you add two <u>positive</u> numbers, the total is greater than 0.

I When you add <u>a positive number</u>, you move to the right along the number line.

K If x is a given positive number, then subtracting <u>the positive number x is the same as adding <u>the</u> negative number ^-x.</u>

L The sum of a positive number $\underline{x}$ and a negative number y is negative <u>only if the two positive numbers x and ^-y satisfy $x < {}^-y$.</u>

Proof: Suppose x is positive, and $x + y < 0$.
Then $0 < x < {}^-y$. **QED**

M If x is a given negative number, then adding <u>the negative number $\underline{x}$ is the same as subtracting <u>the</u> positive number $^-\underline{x}$.</u>

9 *Could you?*

1 The population of the Earth is about 6 billion.
The Isle of Wight has an area of $381 \, \text{km}^2 = 381\,000\,000 \, \text{m}^2$.

$\therefore$ Each person on Earth would have approximately $\frac{381\,000\,000}{6\,000\,000\,000} \, \text{m}^2$ to stand on (provided they all managed to get there!); that is, $0.0635 \, \text{m}^2 = 635 \, \text{cm}^2$.

This would allow each person, on average, a rectangle 40 cm by 16 cm, or 30 cm by 21 cm, which would be just about enough space (especially since a large fraction of the Earth's population consists of children).

2 Swimming pools come in different sizes. A small one with length 10 m, width 3 m, depth 1.5 m contains $10 \times 3 \times 1.5 \,\text{m}^3$ of water.

Each cubic metre contains 1000 litres.

$\therefore$ The pool would contain 45 000 litres of water.

You should drink 1.5 to 2 litres of water per day.
2 litres per day gives $2 \times 365 = 730$ litres per year.
At that rate it would take $\frac{45\,000}{730}$ years ≈ 61 years years, to consume 45 000 litres.

3 A litre container has volume $1000 \,\text{cm}^3$.

$1\,\text{cm} = 10\,\text{mm}$, so $1000 \,\text{cm}^3 = 1\,000\,000 \,\text{mm}^3$.

Grains of rice vary in size, but they are all larger than 1 mm by 1 mm by 1 mm. (Basmati rice can be as much as 5 mm by 2 mm by 2 mm.)

So there is no way one million grains would fit into a one litre container.

4 One toilet roll has roughly 280 sheets; each sheet is about 14 cm long.
$\therefore$ Length of each roll $\approx 280 \times 14\,\text{cm}$

$$\approx 40 \,\text{metres.}$$

$1000 \div 40 = 25$; so you would need about 25 rolls for 1 km.
Provided the rolls are in carrier bags, it should be possible for you to carry this much toilet paper on your own.

5 A 50 g ball of double knitting wool is about 130 m long.
If you had a total length of half a kilometre ($= 500\,\text{m}$) you would have $\frac{500}{130} \approx 4$ balls of wool.
This might be just about enough to knit a jumper for an 8 year old!

6 10 metres per second $= 10 \times 60 \times 60$ metres per hour

$$= 36 \,\text{km per hour}$$

$$\approx 22.5 \,\text{miles per hour.}$$

This is well within the speed limit for a built-up area. (10 metres per second is the speed of a sprinter running the 100 metres.)

Could you?

7 An A4 sheet of paper measures 297 mm by 210 mm.

$$\therefore \text{ Area of 1 sheet} = 297 \times 210 \text{ mm}^2$$
$$\approx 60\,000 \text{mm}^2.$$

The box has four sides, each of which is 150 mm by 100 mm; so these four sides alone have total area of 60 000 mm^2.
Since the box has two other sides (of size 100 mm by 100 mm), there is no way a single A4 sheet would be large enough.

8 Allowing for the mortar between the bricks, each brick uses up about 23 cm in length and 8 cm in height.

A garage has to be about 5 m long, 3 m wide and 2 m high.
5 metres = 500 cm, so you would need about $\frac{500}{23} \approx 22$ bricks for each layer of bricks along one of the long walls.

2 metres = 200 cm, so each of these walls would need to be about $\frac{200}{8} = 25$ bricks high.

∴ Each long wall would use about 22×25, that is, about 550 bricks.

∴ The two long walls alone use up more than 1000 bricks.

∴ 1000 bricks would not be enough (though 1500 bricks might just do).

9 Each tile is about 20 cm wide and has a depth of about 10 cm exposed. (The rest of each tile is used up to allow for overlaps, which are needed to make the roof waterproof.)

As in question **8**, the long side walls will be about 5 m long.
The garage will be about 3 m wide, but a tiled roof has to have a pitched roof, so the tiled area will consist of two sloping rectangles, each about 5 m by 2 m.
Each sloping rectangle would then use about 25×20 tiles.
∴ 1000 tiles would probably be enough.

10 50 paper clips weigh 20 g.
∴ 5000 paper clips weigh 2 kg, which is a possible weight for a cat.

10 *Fractions with a calculator*

Different calculator models work in slightly different ways, so the answers you get will depend to some extent on which calculator you use.

1 **a** Most people would probably agree that $\frac{1}{3}$ seems simpler than $\frac{5}{8}$.

    b $\frac{5}{8} = 0.625$ (stops after three decimal digits)

      $\frac{1}{3} = 0.333\,333\,333$ (goes on until the display is full)

    c $\frac{1}{4} = 0.25$ (stops after two decimal digits)

      $\frac{1}{5} = 0.2$ (stops after one decimal digit)

      $\frac{1}{6} = 0.166\,666\,666$ (goes on until the display is full; some calculators round the last 6 up to a 7)

      $\frac{1}{7} = 0.142\,857\,142$ (goes on until the display is full; some calculators round the last 2 up to a 3).

    The number of digits in each answer varies a lot: some answers are very short, others are so long that the calculator has to chop off the tail (and may round the last digit as well).

2 **a** $\frac{1}{3} = 0.333\,333\,333$; multiplying by 3 gives 0.999 999 999 (whereas you should get $3 \times \frac{1}{3} = 1$).

    b $\frac{1}{23} = 0.043\,478\,26$

      $\frac{2}{23} = 0.086\,956\,521.$

    The answer for $\frac{2}{23} = 2 \times \frac{1}{23}$ should be exactly twice the answer for $\frac{1}{23}$, but it is not! This is because the answers which the calculator gives are approximate. The **exact** answers go on for ever, so the tails have been chopped off, and the remaining decimal has been rounded.

3 **a** $\frac{1}{2} = 0.5$

      $\frac{1}{3} = 0.333\,333\,333\,333\,333\,33\ldots\ldots$ (goes on for ever)

      $\frac{1}{4} = 0.25$ (stops after two decimal digits)

      $\frac{1}{5} = 0.2$ (stops after one decimal digit)

      $\frac{1}{6} = 0.166\,666\,666\,666\,666\,666\ldots\ldots$ (goes on for ever)

      $\frac{1}{7} = 0.142\,857\,142\,857\,142\,857\ldots\ldots$ (goes on for ever repeating the block 142 857).

    b The calculator cannot handle decimals that go on for ever, so it chops off the tail and works with an approximate value instead. The final digit in this approximate value is rounded up if the next (discarded) digit is ≥ 5.

    This is why the decimal approximation which your calculator

uses for $\frac{2}{23}$ may not be exactly twice the decimal approximation it uses for $\frac{1}{23}$.

c $3 \times \frac{1}{3} = 1$

Proof: $3 \times \dfrac{1}{3} = 3 \times (0.333\,333\,333\,333\ldots\ldots \text{for ever})$

$= 0.999\,999\,999\,999\ldots\ldots \text{for ever}$

$\therefore 0.9\dot{9} = 0.999\,999\,999\,999\ldots\ldots \text{for ever} = 1.$ **QED**

4 **a** $\frac{11}{15} + \frac{13}{18} = \frac{131}{90} = 1\frac{41}{90}$.
If you change this to a decimal, you may get 1.455 555 556.

b $\frac{11}{15} = 0.73\dot{3}$, so your calculator will give 0.733 333 333
$\frac{13}{18} = 0.72\dot{2}$, so your calculator will give 0.722 222 222.
If you add the two displays you get 1.455 555 555.

The answers are different because the calculator has replaced the original values $\frac{11}{15}$ and $\frac{13}{18}$ by approximate decimals.
(If you simply work out $(11 \div 15) + (13 \div 18) = ?$, the calculator will probably give 1.455 555 556. This is because it remembers that the next decimal digit in the correct answer is a 5, and so rounds the last digit up to a 6.)

5 A calculator uses two rules to obtain good approximations:

i the display can only show a certain number of digits, so it remembers one extra digit and throws away all the others;

ii it then uses the extra digit to round the last digit in the display.

(Some calculators remember more than one extra digit. This makes it difficult to predict how a calculator will behave.)

6 All calculators make approximations. They treat long and non-terminating decimals as though they have only eight or ten decimal digits; then they round the final digit.
(If you work out $(1 \div 3) \times 3$, most calculators remember for a few steps that the $1 \div 3$ is really $\frac{1}{3}$, and not 0.333 333 333. So they give the correct answer (namely 1) if you immediately multiply by 3, rather than the incorrect answer 0.999 999 999.)

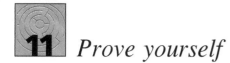

11 *Prove yourself*

1 The square you start with will always look like this for some value of *a*:

a	$a+1$	$a+2$
$a+7$	$a+8$	$a+9$
$a+14$	$a+15$	$a+16$

The nine numbers can then be rearranged to give the magic square below. Each row, column and diagonal adds to $3a + 24$.

$a+15$	a	$a+9$
$a+2$	$a+8$	$a+14$
$a+7$	$a+16$	$a+1$

2
Think of a number	x
Double it	$2x$
Subtract 4	$2x - 4$
Multiply the result by 3	$6x - 12$
Divide by 2	$3x - 6$
Add 6	$3x$
Divide by 3	x .

3 Let the four digits be *a*, *b*, *c*, *d*.
Then the four-digit number '*abcd*' $= 1000a + 100b + 10c + d$.
Reversing the digits gives   '*dcba*' $= 1000d + 100c + 10b + a$.

Adding gives '*abcd*' + '*dcba*' $= (1000a + 100b + 10c + d)$
$$+ (1000d + 100c + 10b + a)$$
$$= 1001a + 110b + 110c + 1001d$$
$$= 11 \times (91a + 91d) + 11 \times (10b + 10c).$$

4 Let the three digits be *a*, *b*, *c*.
Then the three-digit number '*abc*' $= 100a + 10b + c$.
Reversing the digits gives   '*cba*' $= 100c + 10b + a$.

Adding gives '*abc*' + '*cba*' $= (100a + 10b + c) + (100c + 10b + a)$
$$= 101a + 20b + 101c$$
$$= (99a + 22b + 99c) + 2(a - b + c).$$

COMMENTS & SOLUTIONS

The first bracket is always divisible by 11 (since 99 and 22 are divisible by 11).
So the sum on the right-hand side is exactly divisible by 11 precisely when the second bracket $(a - b + c)$ is divisible by 11.

5 Suppose the Fibonacci sequence begins like this: $a, b, \ldots$.
Then the first nine terms are:

$$a, b, b + a, 2b + a, 3b + 2a, 5b + 3a, 8b + 5a, 13b + 8a, 21b + 13a, \ldots$$

a First term plus fifth term $= a + (3b + 2a)$
$$= 3a + 3b = 3(a + b).$$

b, c First term plus ninth term $= a + (21b + 13a)$
$$= 21b + 14a = 7(3b + 2a).$$

 12 *Telephone surveys*

1 **sample** a selection taken from a target population or group.

biased: a sample which fails to represent all the important features of the target population from which it was chosen (for example, by including a larger fraction of some groups than it should).

median: the middle value when items are ranked in order.

response rate: the fraction
(number of replies received) ÷ (number of questionnaires sent out), expressed as a percentage.

subject: the person being interviewed.

chosen at random: picked in an unbiased way from the target population without reference to anything special about each person (for example, if members of the target population are given numbers, subjects can be selected using a random number generator).

random sample: a sample that is chosen at random.

2 The survey changed the target population. The target population should have been **all voters;** but the method used to select the sample changed the target population to **all voters with a car or a phone.** Since those excluded were more likely to vote for one candidate (Roosevelt), the resulting sample was biased.

3 Just over 20%.

4 As the text explains, postal surveys are about one-tenth as expensive to run as face-to-face surveys.

5 Two thirds of the subjects were reached with just one phone call; so once subjects had been chosen, most were contacted very easily. Chasing up the rest meant that 98% of subjects were reached after at most five phone calls.

6 The most serious feature is that only those who feel strongly one way or the other are likely to respond. If the audience is already biased (for example, if the broadcast is transmitted at a strange time, or on a channel with a particular audience, or if most readers or listeners are young), the response to such a poll can be especially unreliable.

7 The very poor might not have a phone, and the very rich might be ex-directory (or have someone else who answers the phone so that the interviewer never gets through to the intended subject). Every experiment or survey is approximate, and so has a **margin of error**. A well-designed experiment or survey makes sure that, though this margin of error is bound to affect the results, it is small enough not to affect the conclusions.
So as long as the number of people excluded in this way is smaller than the margin of error of the survey, the result can still be useful.

8 A low response rate suggests that only those who felt strongly made the effort to respond. This lays the survey open to the weaknesses indicated in the solution to question **6**.

9 **a** To make sure that every subject is treated in the same way.

b Yes – for the same reasons. (They usually do: but they have to learn it by heart, whereas the telephone interviewers can keep the script in front of them and just read it.)

 13 *Probably right, but ...*

Common sense arguments are often wrong. To decide correctly you have to **calculate**. The key idea here is to:

- identify the different **equally likely outcomes**,
- then count how many of these outcomes are **favourable**.

1   When a coin is tossed twice, there are **four** possible outcomes –
    HH, HT, TH, TT – which are all equally likely. A head appears in
    three of these, so there are four possible outcomes, three of which
    are favourable: the probablity of getting at least one head is $\frac{3}{4}$.

2   With two children, there are **four** possibilities – BB (boy first and
    boy second), BG, GB, GG. Since Mr Patel has at least one boy,
    we are left with just three possibilities – BB, BG, or GB. Since
    roughly half of all births are boys and half are girls, these three
    possiblities are (roughly) equally likely. In only one of the three is
    the other child a boy. Since we know that Mr Patel has at least
    one boy, there are three possible outcomes (BB, BG or GB), only
    one of which (BB) is favourable: the probability is $\frac{1}{3}$.

3   When tossing three coins (coin 1, coin 2 and coin 3) there are
    eight possible outcomes – HHH, HHT, HTH, HTT, THH, THT,
    TTH, TTT – which are all equally likely. In only **two** of these do
    the coins all come down the same, so the probability is $\frac{2}{8} = \frac{1}{4}$.

4   There are **six** possible outcomes (1, 2, 3, 4, 5, 6). Of these three
    are prime numbers (2, 3, 5) and three are even numbers (2, 4, 6);
    but 2 is both prime and even, so there are just **five** outcomes
    which are either prime or even. So the probability that Ben scores
    a point is $\frac{5}{6}$.

5   Imagine that the three counters are red (XX), white (XO) and blue
    (OO). Each counter has two sides, so there are exactly six
    possible outcomes – choose any one of three counters, and then
    lay it down on the table in one of two possible ways – (red, X),
    (red, X), (white, X), (white, O), (blue, O), (blue, O).
    (Note that the first two of these outcomes look the same; but they
    are mathematically different.)
    These six outcomes are all equally likely.
    You are told that when the counter is laid on the table, it shows a
    cross; there are just **three** possible ways this could happen:
    (red, X), (red, X), (white, X).
    Among these three ways, there are **two** where the other side of
    the counter is also a cross, so the probability is $\frac{2}{3}$.

6   Make two tables – one listing the totals for two ordinary dice and
    one listing the totals for the strange dice in the question:

+	1	2	3	4	5	6
1	2	3	4	5	6	7
2	3	4	5	6	7	8
3	4	5	6	7	8	9
4	5	6	7	8	9	10
5	6	7	8	9	10	11
6	7	8	9	10	11	12

+	1	2	2	3	3	4
1	2	3	3	4	4	5
3	4	5	5	6	6	7
4	5	6	6	7	7	8
5	6	7	7	8	8	9
6	7	8	8	9	9	10
8	9	10	10	11	11	12

Notice that each table produces the same totals 2, 3, 4, 5, 6, 7, 8, 9, 10, 11, 12, and that each total occurs with the same frequency (2 occurs just once, 3 occurs just twice, and so on). So the strange dice give the same totals, each total occurring with exactly the same probability as with two ordinary dice.

14 *Magic squares*

1 Suppose the integers 1, 2, 3, 4 could be arranged in a 2 by 2 square array to make a magic square of order 2.
The '1' must go in one of the four corners. And each corner lies in one row and in one column.
But the number in the same **row** as 1 cannot be the same as the number in the same **column** as 1.
∴ The row and column sums cannot be the same.

You can write this very simply using algebra:
Let the number in the bottom left corner be a, the number above it b and the number to its right c.
Then the column sum is $a + b$ and the row sum is $a + c$.
For a magic square these must be equal: $a + b = a + c$, so $b = c$.

2 b There are four rotated versions (through $0°$, $90°$, $180°$, $270°$), and four reflected versions (in the four dotted mirrors) – giving eight altogether.

3 Here is one example.

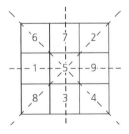

4

16	2	3	13
5	11	10	8
9	7	6	12
4	14	15	1

5 a Your two answers should be equal.

b Again, your two answers should be equal.

6 a The magic constant is 65.

19	21	3	10	12
25	2	9	11	18
1	8	15	17	24
7	14	16	23	5
13	20	22	4	6

b

33	42	44	4	13	15	24
41	43	3	12	21	23	32
49	2	11	20	22	31	40
1	10	19	28	30	39	48
9	18	27	29	38	47	7
17	26	35	37	46	6	8
25	34	36	45	5	14	16

7 a Order 3: 15. Order 4: 34. Order 5: 65.

b If you add up all the entries in the square in two different ways, the two answers must be equal!

i The entries in a magic square of order n are the positive integers

$$1, 2, 3, 4, 5, \ldots, n^2.$$

If you add up all these numbers in the obvious way (using the formula for triangular numbers) you get

$$1 + 2 + 3 + 4 + 5 + \ldots + n^2 = \tfrac{1}{2}n^2(n^2 + 1).$$

ii You can also add up the numbers in the square one row at a time. The entries in each row sum to the magic constant M. There are n rows, so the total will be $n \times M$.

$$\therefore \quad n \times M = \tfrac{1}{2}n^2(n^2 + 1)$$
$$\therefore \quad M = \tfrac{1}{2}n(n^2 + 1).$$

8 a Let the magic constant be M.

The numbers in the square are the integers from 1 to 9, so their sum must equal $1 + 2 + 3 + \ldots + 9 = 45$.

Another way of adding up all the numbers in the square is to add the numbers in each of the three rows.

Each row has sum M, so the sum of the numbers in all three rows is $M + M + M = 3M$.

$$\therefore \quad 45 = 3M, \text{ so } M = 15.$$

b Let the number in the central square be c.

Each of the four lines through the central square (row, column, and two diagonals) has sum equal to $M = 15$.

So adding up the entries in these four lines gives a total of $4 \times 15 = 60$.

These four lines use up each of the numbers 1–9 once each – except for the central number c, which occurs four times (once in each line).

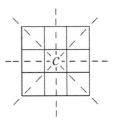

$$\therefore \quad 60 = (1 + 2 + 3 + \ldots + 9) + 3c$$
$$= 45 + 3c$$
$$\therefore \quad c = 5.$$

c The only pairs which combine with 9 to make a sum of 15 are

$$5 + 1 \, (+9 = 15) \text{ and } 4 + 2 \, (+9 = 15).$$

Each corner square lies in **three** lines, each of which has a total of 15. So 9 cannot go in a corner.

d 9 must go in the centre of some edge – say the centre square of the left-hand column.

Then 1 has to go in the centre square of the right-hand column. The other numbers in the left-hand column must be 4 and 2 – so you can put 4 in the top left corner and 2 in the bottom left corner.

The rest of the magic square is then determined.

9 All fifteen lines, five in each direction, sum to 38.

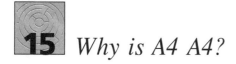

15 Why is A4 A4?

1,2 The first and third rectangles have the same value for (length ÷ width); so do the second and fourth rectangles.

3 Let the length and width of the first rectangle be l and w.
Then for the first and third rectangles (length ÷ width) $= l/w$, and for the second and fourth rectangles (length ÷ width) $= w/(l/2)$
$$= 2w/l.$$
These will be equal precisely when $l/w = 2w/l$; that is when $(l/w)^2 = 2$, or when $l/w = \sqrt{2}$.

4 See solution to question **5**.

5 a A4: 297 mm by 210 mm; A5: 210 mm by 148 mm; A6: 148 mm by 105 mm.

   b (Length ÷ width) = A4 : 297/210 = 1.414 285 71 . . .
   A5 : 210/148 = 1.418 918 91 . . .
   A6 : 148/105 = 1.409 523 8 . . . .

   c $\sqrt{2} = 1.414\ 213\ 56 \ldots$.

   d A3 folded gives A4, so A3 must be 420 mm by 297 mm (approx).
   A2 folded gives A3, so A2 must be 594 mm by 420 mm.
   Similarly A1: 840 mm by 594 mm; A0: 1188 mm by 840 mm.

   e Approximate area of A0 sheet $= 1.188 \times 0.840\,\text{m}^2$
   $$= 0.997\,92\,\text{m}^2.$$
   This is almost 1 square metre.

6 Let the required dimensions of an A0 sheet be l metres by w metres.
Then $l/w = \sqrt{2}$ and $l \times w = 1$.
Substitute $w = 1/l$ into the first equation to get $l^2 = \sqrt{2}$.
$$\therefore \quad l = \sqrt{(\sqrt{2})} = \sqrt[4]{2} = 1.189\,207\,11 \ldots$$
and $\quad w = 1/(\sqrt[4]{2}) = 0.840\,896\,41 \ldots$.
So an A0 sheet should be approximately 1189 mm by 841 mm.

7 The large triangle is an isosceles right-angled triangle with short side of length 210 mm and hypotenuse of length 297 mm.
The next smaller triangle is an isosceles right-angled triangle with short side of length 148 mm and hypotenuse of length 210 mm.
The smallest triangle is an isosceles right-angled triangle with short side of length 105 mm and hypotenuse of length 148 mm.

All three triangles are similar.

It is clear (from the way the square was folded) that the short side of the first triangle is equal to the width of the original A4 sheet, but it is surprising that the length of the hypotenuse of this triangle is equal to the length of the 'original' A4 sheet of paper.

8   The answer depends on the width of an A0 sheet of paper (840 mm or 841 mm). The largest square that can be cut from an A0 sheet is 840 mm by 840 mm (or 841 mm by 841 mm). The length of the diagonal of this largest square is 1188 mm (or 1189 mm).

9   **a** Length of hypotentuse: 297 mm; 210 mm; 148 mm.
     Length of shorter sides: 210 mm; 148 mm; 105 mm.

     b Each ratio is approximately equal to $\sqrt{2}$.

     c $\sqrt{2} = 1.414\,213\,56\ldots$ is very close to the answer in **b**.

     d $h'' = 297$, $h' = 210$, $h = 148$.
     $h'' \div h'$ and $h' \div h$ are almost equal, and are both very close to $\sqrt{2}$.

10   For example: suppose an A4 sheet has length l mm and width w mm; then the long thin rectangle is **similar to** an $(l + w)$ by w rectangle.

16   *Rules for number sequences*

1   **a** Add 3, add 6, add 9, add 12, ...

2   At first this may not be clear, because the rule does not explain how to get the second term. One way to try to make sense of the problem is to look at the **difference** between successive terms. This gives the term-to-term rule:

     (add 2), add 2, add 4, add 6, add 10, add 16, ...

     Except for the first step, the adding rule is given **by the sequence itself!** So the next three terms are 68, 110, 178, given by

     add 26, add 42, add 68.

     Each term of the sequence is equal to the sum of the two previous terms.

You may have met this idea before in the famous **Fibonacci** sequence

$$0, 1, 1, 2, 3, 5, 8, 13, 21, 34, 55, 89, \ldots .$$

3 a This could be described as

   i the sequence 3, 6, 9 repeated over and over again, or as

   ii the sequence generated by the term-to-term rules

   add 3, add 3, subtract 6, add 3, add 3, subtract 6, ...

b Multiples of 3: 3×1, 3×2, 3×3, 3×4, ...

c Add 3, add 3, subtract 3, add 3, add 3, subtract 3, ...

d Double, add 3, double, add 3, double, ...

e Add 3, add 3, add 4, add 4, add 5, add 5, ...

f Add 3, add 3, add 5, add 5, add 7, add 7, ...

g Add 3, add 3, add 4, add 4, add 4, add 5, add 5, add 5, add 5, add 6, ...

h Add 3, add 3, add 6, add 6, add 9, add 9, ...

i Fibonacci-like: start with 3, 6, ...; then calculate each term as the sum of the two previous terms.

4 a 10.

   b Claim: There are $n(n + 1)/2$ unit squares in the nth staircase. **Proof**: Take **two** copies of the nth staircase, turn one upside down, and then fit them together to make an n by $n + 1$ rectangle. **QED**

5 One way to get started is to count the shaded squares in the first few diagrams of the sequence. This produces the first few terms of a **sequence of numbers.** If you look at this sequence of numbers, you may come up with a guess about how the sequence continues. But this is **only a guess!**

You have to discover the **actual** numbers produced by the sequence of **diagrams**. So you have to go back to the sequence of diagrams and explain why it produces the numbers you expect. For example, in question **4** the **number** sequence 0, 1, 3, 6, ... suggests the rule

$$\text{add } 1, \text{add } 2, \text{add } 3, \ldots .$$

This suggests that the next number could be 10. But it does not prove it! To see that the next number really is 10 you have to go back to the **diagrams** and see that

- the second diagram is obtained from the first by adding a column of 2 unit squares on the right;

- the third diagram is obtained from the second by adding a column of 3 unit squares on the right; and

- the nth diagram is obtained from the one before it by adding an extra column of n unit squares on the right.

a **Claim**: Number of shaded squares in the nth diagram $= 3n - 2$.
Proof: To get the nth diagram from the previous diagram, you always add 3 squares: one on the end of each of the three arms of the T-shape.
To get from the first diagram (1 square) to the nth takes $n - 1$ steps.

$\therefore$ Number of shaded squares in the nth diagram
$= 1 + 3(n - 1) = 3n - 2$. **QED**

b **Claim**: Number of shaded squares in the nth diagram $= 4n - 3$.
Proof: To get the nth diagram from the previous diagram, you always add 4 squares, one on the end of each of the four arms of the $+$ shape.
To get from the first diagram (1 square) to the nth takes $n - 1$ steps.
$\therefore$ Number of shaded squares in the nth diagram
$= 1 + 4(n - 1) = 4n - 3$. **QED**

c **Claim**: Number of shaded squares in the nth diagram $= n^2$.
Proof: The third diagram has three rows containing 1, 3 and 5 squares.
Similarly the nth diagram has n rows containing 1, 3, 5, ... , $2n - 1$ squares.
So the number of squares in the nth diagram is equal to

$$1 + 3 + 5 + \ldots (2n - 1).$$

Numerical examples suggest that this sum is always equal to n^2 – but it is not clear why this should always be true. However, notice that you can always cut the nth diagram into two pieces, and that the right-hand piece, when turned through exactly $180°$, fits exactly into the hole in the bottom left corner to make an n by n square.

Rules for number sequences   77

You can write this out using algebra:

- the left-hand piece is (an upside down copy of) the nth staircase in question **4**, so has $n(n+1)/2$ squares;

- the right-hand piece is (an upside down copy of) the $(n-1)$th staircase in question **4**, so has $(n-1)n/2$ squares.

$\therefore$ The nth diagram contains

$$\frac{n(n+1)}{2} + \frac{(n-1)n}{2} = n^2 \text{ squares. } \textbf{QED}$$

d Claim: Number of shaded squares in nth diagram
$$= (n-1)^2 + n^2.$$
Proof: Cut the nth diagram with a horizontal cut just above the central row of $2n-1$ squares.
Then the larger lower part is precisely the nth diagram in part **c**, so has n^2 squares;
and the smaller upper part is (an upside down copy of) the $(n-1)$th diagram in part **c**, so has $(n-1)^2$ squares. **QED**

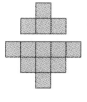

e Claim: Number of shaded squares in nth diagram
$$= (n-1)^2 + n^2.$$
Proof: Split the diagram just above the diagonal. Now turn the two pieces through $45°$ clockwise. The large piece is then just like the nth diagram in part **c**, so has n^2 squares; and the small piece is just like (an upside down copy of) the $(n-1)$th diagram in part **c**, so has $(n-1)^2$ squares. **QED**

17 *Area*

1 a Enclose the kite in an a by b rectangle. The area of this enclosing rectangle is ab.
The two diagonals cut the rectangle into four small rectangles, and cut the kite into four triangles.
The top left corner rectangle of the large rectangle contains two copies of the top left triangular part of the kite; the same thing happens in the other corners.
So the kite contains half of each corner rectangle.

$$\therefore \text{ Area of kite} = \tfrac{1}{2}(\text{area of rectangle}) = \tfrac{1}{2}ab.$$

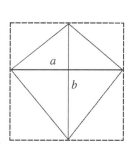

b The same argument works for any quadrilateral in which the diagonals are perpendicular, so if the diagonals have lengths a and b, the area of such a quadrilateral is equal to $\tfrac{1}{2}ab$.

2 **Claim**: There are **six** different sized rectangles.
Proof: Let the rectangles have sides of lengths a cm and b cm.
$P = 2a + 2b$, $A = ab$, and $A = 3P$, so we must solve the equation

$$ab = A = 3P = 6a + 6b$$
$$\therefore \quad ab - 6a - 6b = 0.$$

If we now add 36 to each side, the left-hand side factorises
nicely:

$$\therefore \quad ab - 6a - 6b + 36 = 36$$
$$\therefore \quad (a - 6)(b - 6) = 36.$$

This is useful only because you are told that the side lengths a
and b are **integers;** so $a - 6$ and $b - 6$ are integers whose product
equals 36. There are just six possibilities:

  i $a - 6 = 36$, $b - 6 = 1$: $a = 42$, $b = 7$;

  ii $a - 6 = 18$, $b - 6 = 2$: $a = 24$, $b = 8$;

  iii $a - 6 = 12$, $b - 6 = 3$: $a = 18$, $b = 9$;

  iv $a - 6 = 9$, $b - 6 = 4$: $a = 15$, $b = 10$;

  v $a - 6 = 6$, $b - 6 = 6$: $a = 12$, $b = 12$;

  vi $a - 6 = -6$, $b - 6 = -6$: $a = 0$, $b = 0$.

3 Cut the arrowhead into two congruent triangles (along the
horizontal diameter through the centre of the circle and the tip of
the arrowhead).
Each triangle has base of length r and height $\frac{1}{2}r$.

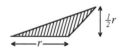

$\therefore$ Each triangle has area $= \frac{1}{2} \times r \times (\frac{1}{2}r) = \frac{1}{4}r^2$.

$\therefore$ The complete arrowhead has area $= \frac{1}{2}r^2$.

4 **a** **Claim**: The rectangle of largest area has
         length = breadth = 6 units.
     Proof: Suppose the perimeter $P = 24$ units. If the sides of the
     rectangle have lengths a units and b units, then
        $P = 2a + 2b = 24$.
     $\therefore b = 12 - a$.

     You want to know how big the area $A = ab$ can be.

     $A = ab$
       $= a(12 - a)$
       $= 36 - (a^2 - 12a + 36)$

Area 79

$$= 36 - (a-6)^2$$

$$\leq 36 \qquad \text{(since a squared term like } (a-6)^2 \text{ is never negative).}$$

So the area A can never be greater than 36 square units. And $A = 36$ when $a = 6$. **QED**

b For the triangle to have the largest possible area, the triangle must be equilateral: that is, all three sides must have the same length 8 units. It is not easy to prove this.

c It is said that Queen Dido stretched the long thin strip to form a semicircle, with the seashore as a diameter. This does in fact enclose the largest possible area, but a proof of this fact is hard.

18 *Very large*

1 **a** The diameter of the Sun is $\frac{1\,329\,000}{12\,735}$ times as big as that of the Earth. That is, just over 100 times as big.
If the Sun is modelled by an orange (radius roughly 5 cm), then the Earth would be modelled by a sphere of radius $\frac{5}{100}$ times as big, that is, by a sphere of radius 0.05 cm (for example, by a very small grain of rice).

b The question tells you that the Sun has diameter roughly 1 400 000 km, so it has a radius roughly 700 000 km, and that the Sun is modelled by an orange (radius roughly 5 cm).

The Earth is 150 000 000 km from the Sun.

Let the correct position of the model of the Earth be x cm from the orange.

$$\therefore \quad x : 5 = 150\,000\,000 : 700\,000$$
$$\therefore \quad x \quad = 7500 : 7 \approx 1100.$$

So the model of the Earth should be positioned about 11 metres from the orange.

c The number of seconds in 4.24 years is

$$4.24 \times 365 \times 24 \times 60 \times 60,$$

which is just over 130 000 000 (or 1.3×10^8).
This is the number of seconds required for light to travel from Proxima Centauri to Earth.

Since light takes only 500 seconds to travel from the Sun to Earth, the distance from the Earth to Proxima Centauri is roughly $\frac{130\,000\,000}{500}$ times as far as the distance from the Sun to Earth; that is, roughly 260 000 times as far as the distance from the Sun to Earth.

So if in the model the Sun (= orange) is 11 m away from the Earth (= small grain of rice), then Proxima Centauri should be $260\,000 \times 11\text{m} = 260 \times 11\,\text{km} = 2860$ km away.

2 You are told that the average human being weighs between 40 kg and 100 kg. Suppose the average human being weighs 70 kg.

∴ Total weight of six billion people is approximately

$$6\,000\,000\,000 \times 70\,\text{kg} = 420\,000\,000\,\text{tonnes}.$$

This is about two thirds of the estimated total weight of krill.

3 Almost all human beings are less than 2 m tall. So stretched end to end,

total length of krill $= 600\,000\,000\,000\,000 \times 5\,\text{cm} = 3 \times 10^{10}\,\text{km}$;

total length of human beings $< 6\,000\,000\,000 \times 2\,\text{m} = 12 \times 10^6\,\text{km}$.

4 For example, assuming the given information is correct, human beings catch 70 million tonnes of fish each year: that is enough for the average human being to eat one sixth of his body weight in fish each year!

5 What appears in successive displays as you repeatedly square will depend on your calculator, but you are likely to see

6;	36;	1296;	1 679 616;
2.8211 12;	7.9586 24;	6.334 49;	4.0119 99 .

The last one (which is the calculator's lazy way of writing 4.0119×10^{99}) is likely to be the biggest that your calculator can handle in the display.

6 The display 4.0119×10^{99} is an approximate value for 6^{128}.

7 **a** The largest number you can enter will depend on the type of calculator, but it is likely to be of the form $9.999\,999\,9 \times 10^{99}$.

  b The square of this number is roughly $99.999\,999\,8 \times 10^{198}$. Written out in full, this is roughly equal to a number starting with 1 followed by 200 zeros.

8 $\frac{1}{3} \times \pi \times 8^2 \times 16 = 1072.329\ldots$ cubic kilometres.

9 Every 1000 years the bird wears away 1 cubic millimetre.
You know that $10\,\text{mm} = 1\,\text{cm}$, $100\,\text{cm} = 1\,\text{m}$, and $1000\,\text{m} = 1\,\text{km}$;

$\therefore\quad 1\,\text{km} = 10 \times 100 \times 1000\,\text{mm}$,

so there are $(10 \times 100 \times 1000)^3$ cubic millimetres in 1 cubic kilometre.

$\therefore\quad$ 1000 cubic kilometres
$= 1000 \times (10 \times 100 \times 1000)^3$ cubic millimetres.

The bird wears away 1 cubic millimetre every **1000** years.

$\therefore\quad$ It will take $\mathbf{1000} \times (1000 \times (10 \times 100 \times 1000)^3)$ years,
that is 10^{24} years, for the bird to wear away the mountain.

10 This is unimaginably longer than the age of the universe (which is roughly 10^{10} years).

11 The solution to question **9** uses the fact that the bird visits the mountain once every **1000** years.
If the bird visits the mountain every Y years, then the rest of the calculation is exactly the same as in question **9**, so it would take

$$Y \times (1000 \times (10 \times 100 \times 1000)^3) = Y \times 10^{21} \text{ years}$$

for the bird to wear away the mountain.
So you have to choose the value of Y to make $Y \times 10^{21}$ equal to the age of the universe:

$$Y \times 10^{21} = 10^{10}$$
$$\therefore Y \times 10^{11} = 1.$$

The bird would have to visit the mountain 10^{11} times every year, which works out at one visit every $0.000\,314$ seconds!

Three coins in a line

1 a The move S changes **H H H** to **T H T**;
   the move R then changes **T H T** to **T T H**.
   So $S*R = L$.

   b The move S changes **H H H** to **T H T**;
   the move L then changes **T H T** to **H T T**.
   So $S*L = R$.

2 a The move R changes **H H H** to **H T T**;
   the move L then changes **H T T** to **T H T**.
   So $R*L = S$.

   b $R*L = S$, and $L*R = S$; so $R*L = L*R$.

3 a $R*L = S$
   $\therefore R*L*R = S*R$.

   And $S*R = L$ (from question **1a**).
   $\therefore R*L*R = L$.

   b $L*R = S$
   $\therefore L*R*L = S*L$.

   And $S*L = R$ (from question **1b**).
   So $L*R*L = R$.

4 a $R*R$ leaves the coins exactly as they started.

   b $L*L$ leaves the coins exactly as they started.

5

	Second move			
	I	*L*	*R*	*S*
I	*I*	*L*	*R*	*S*
L	*L*	*I*	*S*	*R*
R	*R*	*S*	*I*	*L*
S	*S*	*R*	*L*	*I*

First move

6 a R **b** R **c** I **d** I **e** S **f** I **g** S **h** I

7 a 4.

   b **Claim**: It is not possible to change **H H H** to **T T T**.
   Proof: **H H H** shows an odd number of heads.
   Each of the moves L, R, S changes an arrangement showing an
   odd number of heads into another arrangement showing an
   odd number of heads.
   So you can never get **T T T**. **QED**

20 *Three by three revisited*

A **a** Three. The square removed must be either:

    i   a corner square, or

    ii   the central square, or

    iii a square in the middle of an edge.

b Eight. There is only one centre square. So if you remove two squares, one of the two has to be either a corner square or in the middle of an edge.

- Suppose first that one of the squares removed is a corner square, say the top left corner. If the second square is top centre, top right, centre, centre right, or bottom right you get five non-congruent shapes. (If the second square is one of the other three squares you get another shape congruent to one of these five.)

- It remains to count those shapes obtained by removing two squares, **neither of which is a corner square**. One of the two squares removed must then be from the middle of an edge, say the centre square of the top edge. The second square could then be the central square, or the centre of the right edge, or the centre of the bottom edge, giving three non-congruent shapes.

B **a** Six.

    i   sixteen 1 by 1s;

    ii   one 2 by 2 and twelve 1 by 1s;

    iii two 2 by 2s and eight 1 by 1s;

    iv three 2 by 2s and four 1 by 1s;

    v   four 2 by 2s;

    vi one 3 by 3 and seven 1 by 1s.

b Twenty.

    i   nine 1 by 1s;

    ii   one 2 by 1, and seven 1 by 1s;

    iii two 2 by 1s and five 1 by 1s;

    iv three 2 by 1s and three 1 by 1s;

    v   four 2 by 1s and one 1 by 1;

vi one 3 by 1 and six 1 by 1s;

vii one 3 by 1, one 2 by 1, and four 1 by 1s;

viii one 3 by 1, two 2 by 1s, and two 1 by 1s;

ix one 3 by 1, and three 2 by 1s;

x two 3 by 1s and three 1 by 1s;

xi two 3 by 1s, one 2 by 1, and one 1 by 1;

xii three 3 by 1s;

xiii one 2 by 2 and five 1 by 1s;

xiv one 2 by 2, one 2 by 1, and three 1 by 1s;

xv one 2 by 2, two 2 by 1s, and one 1 by 1;

xvi one 2 by 2, one 3 by 1, and two 1 by 1s;

xvii one 2 by 2, one 3 by 1, and one 2 by 1;

xviii one 3 by 2, and three 1 by 1s;

xix one 3 by 2, one 2 by 1, and one 1 by 1;

xx one 3 by 2, and one 3 by 1.

C Yes; sixteen moves.

Four moves shift the knights to the second arrangement shown here.

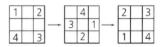

A further four moves are then needed to get to the third arrangement.

At this stage, after eight moves, the four knights have managed a quarter turn anticlockwise.

The next quarter turn requires eight more moves.

To see that the exchange cannot be done more quickly notice that no knight can ever use the central square – so throw it away, leaving just eight squares.

Call two squares *neighbours* if it is possible to get from one to the other by a knight's move.

Then the remaining eight squares form a single cycle

a	d	g
f		b
c	h	e

$$a \to b \to c \to d \to e \to f \to g \to h \to a.$$

The knights are forced to move round this cycle. Each knight has to move on round the cycle to make room for the next knight to move in behind it; so all the knights have to move round the cycle in the same direction.

Three by three revisited   85

D Four.

Observe first (by trial and error) that you can certainly cut the 3 by 3 square into **four** pieces, no two of which are congruent.

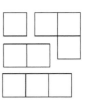

But why is this the best possible?
To get a large number of pieces, the average area of each piece must be small.
Any two 1 by 1s are congruent, so there can be at most one 1 by 1 piece. Similarly, there can be at most one 2 by 1 piece.
The large square has area 9 square units and $9 = 1 + 2 + 3 + 3$, so if you are lucky you might just manage to cut the 3 by 3 square into one 1 by 1, one 2 by 1 and two pieces of area 3. But the two pieces of area 3 must be non-congruent, so one piece must be a 3 by 1 and the other an L-shape.

E • The uncoloured square starts out with lots of symmetries. Colouring squares can spoil existing symmetries, but cannot introduce new symmetries.
The uncoloured square has no rotation of order 3.
∴ Each combination in row **3** of the table is impossible.

	0	1	2	3	4
1	·	·	·	·	·
2	·	·	·	·	·
3	×	×	×	×	×
4	·	·	·	·	✓

• The uncoloured square has exactly four lines of reflection symmetry.
Any pattern with all four lines of symmetry automatically has a rotation of order 4.
∴ Only the last entry in column **4** is possible.

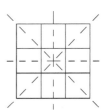

Any pattern with three of these lines of symmetry automatically has the fourth line of symmetry.
∴ Each entry in column **3** is impossible.

	0	1	2	3	4
1	·	·	·	×	×
2	·	·	·	×	×
3	·	·	·	×	×
4	·	·	·	×	✓

• If a pattern has a line of symmetry and admits a rotation of order $r \geq 2$, then it has at least r lines of symmetry.
∴ The last three entries in column **1** are impossible, and the last two entries in column **2** are impossible.

	0	1	2	3	4
1	·	·	·	·	·
2	·	×	·	·	·
3	·	×	×	·	·
4	·	×	×	·	✓

Similarly if a pattern has two lines of symmetry, then it admits a rotation of order ≥ 2.
∴ first entry in column **2** is impossible.

This leaves just **five** combinations which **might** be possible. Four of the five really occur for a suitable colouring of the 3 by 3 square. One of the five is impossible for a colouring of the 3 by 3 square, but can occur for a colouring of the 4 by 4 square. Which is it?

	0	1	2	3	4
1	·	·	×	×	×
2	·	×	·	×	×
3	×	×	×	×	×
4	·	×	×	×	✓

21 Puzzles

1 The sum of the angles in a decagon is $(10 - 2) \times 180°$.
∴ the average size for the 10 angles is $144°$.
Each right angle is $54°$ smaller than the required average of $144°$, so we cannot have very many of them.

If the decagon is **convex** (that is, with no inward pointing corners), each angle is less than $180°$, and the largest possible number of right angles is **three**.

If the decagon is allowed to have corners pointing inwards (and so have internal angles greater than $180°$), the largest possible number of internal right angles is **seven**.

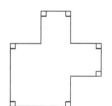

2 a Let the middle integer (the second of the three) be called n. Then the three consecutive integers are $n - 1$, n, and $n + 1$, and their sum is equal to $(n - 1) + n + (n + 1) = 3n$. This is clearly a multiple of 3.

b Let the middle integer (the third of the five) be called n. Then the five consecutive integers are $n - 2$, $n - 1$, n, $n + 1$ and $n + 2$ and their sum is equal to
$$(n - 2) + (n - 1) + n + (n + 1) + (n + 2) = 5n.$$
This is clearly a multiple of 5.

c Let the smallest of the four integers be called n. Then the four consecutive integers are n, $n + 1$, $n + 2$, and $n + 3$. and their sum is equal to $n + (n + 1) + (n + 2) + (n + 3) = 4n + 6$. This is certainly *even* (since $4n + 6 = 2(2n + 3)$), but is **never** a multiple of 4 (since $2n$ is even, so $2n + 3$ is always odd). For example, $1 + 2 + 3 + 4 = 10$ is not a multiple of 4.

COMMENTS & SOLUTIONS

3 Let the two colours be red and yellow, and consider all possible combinations.

> 0 red sections and 6 yellow: **1** way;
>
> 1 red sections and 5 yellow: **6** ways;
>
> 2 red sections and 4 yellow: **15** ways (6 with two red together, 6 with one yellow section in between the reds; 3 with two yellows in between);
>
> 3 red sections and 3 yellow: **20** ways;
>
> 4 red sections and 2 yellow: **15** ways;
>
> 5 red sections and 1 yellow: **6** ways;
>
> 6 red sections and 0 yellow: **1** way.

This gives a total of 64 ways to colour the six sections in two colours.

Each such cap can be combined with either a red peak or a yellow peak – giving 64×2 ways altogether.

At this point you should notice that $128 = 2^7$, which suggests a much quicker solution.
There are seven things to colour (6 sections and 1 peak).
Each can be either red or yellow – giving $2 \times 2 \times 2 \times 2 \times 2 \times 2 \times 2$ different ways.

4 a Folding the circle in half produces a fold line which is a diameter. If you fold the circle in half again using a different fold line, then the centre should be where the two diameters meet.

  The problem with this method is that, since we do not know the fold line in advance, the basic move 'fold the circle in half' is approximate. So the method is only slightly better than 'put a dot where you think the centre should be'.

  b Let the given circle be called $\mathscr{C}$.
  Choose two points P and A on the circumference of the circle $\mathscr{C}$. Use the compasses to draw the circle with centre P and passing through the point A; let this new circle meet the original circle $\mathscr{C}$ at the points A and B.

  Now use the compasses to find the angle bisector PQ of the angle $\angle APB$.
  (Draw the circle with centre A which goes through the point P, and the circle with centre B which goes through the point P.

These two circles meet at P and Q.
Triangles PQA and PQB are congruent, by the SSS
congruence criterion.

$\therefore \quad \angle APQ = \angle BPQ$.

$\therefore \quad PQ$ is the bisector of $\angle APB$.)

Extend the line segment PQ past Q until it cuts the original
circle $\mathscr{C}$ again at R. Then PR is a diameter.

(To prove this you need to know about cyclic quadrilaterals.
Triangles PRA and PRB are congruent, by the SAS
congruence criterion.

$\therefore \quad \angle RAP = \angle RBP$.

Since $PARB$ is a cyclic quadrilateral, $\angle RAP + \angle RBP = 180°$.

$\therefore \quad \angle RAP = 90°$, so PR is a diameter.)

Finally use the compasses to find the midpoint of PR: this is
the required centre.

5   You are told that there were two trains each hour. If the trains left
every half hour, Mike would have expected to travel via Horsham
roughly half the time. Since this is not what happened, we can be
sure that the train times were not equally spaced.

Mike turned up randomly, but nearly always arrived in the gap
after the Hove train had left and before the Horsham train arrived.
So this gap must have been considerably longer than the gap after
the Horsham train had left and before the Hove train arrived.
(For example, the Hove train might have left each hour on the
hour, with the Horsham train leaving at quarter to each hour.)

6   Mount Everest is just under 10 km high.
If the Earth is represented by a football, the Earth's diameter of
around 13 000 km is scaled down to around 30 cm.

$\therefore \quad$ 10 km would be scaled down to $\frac{30}{1300}$ cm, or 0.25 mm.

If the football was a very smooth sphere, then your fingers would
certainly feel a sharp spike of height 0.25 mm. But you might not
notice it if it was just a bump.

7   Placing coins randomly on two piles is like tossing Heads and
Tails. So this problem is the same as asking for the probability of
tossing three Heads **before we get two Tails**.

The only ways of doing this are to toss either

i HHH straight off, or

ii one of THHH, HTHH, HHTH.

The probability of **i** is $\left(\frac{1}{2}\right)^3 = \frac{1}{8}$. And each of the events in **ii** has probability $\left(\frac{1}{2}\right)^4 = \frac{1}{16}$. So the total probability is $\frac{1}{8} + \frac{3}{16} = \frac{5}{16}$.

8 To work out how much longer the second loop is, you do not need to know the actual value of the radius of the Earth.
Let the radius of the Earth be r metres.
Then the circumference of the equator is $2\pi r$ metres; this is the length of the first wire loop.
The second wire loop is a circle of radius $(r + 1)$ metres, so it has length $2\pi(r + 1)$ metres – which is exactly 2π metres longer than the first loop.

EXTRA 1

Centrefold

The folded rectangle has perimeter equal to three sides of the original square. So the original square has sides of length 4 cm and has area 16 cm².

EXTRA 2

Spot the pattern

$100 = 10^2$ will be at the end of the 10th row.

The 10th row contains $10^2 - 9^2 = 19 = 2 \times 10 - 1$ integers;
∴ the next row contains $2 \times 10 + 1$ integers;
∴ the number directly below 100 is 120.

1000 is in the 32nd row, so the number directly below 1000 is 1064.

EXTRA 3

Greek cross

EXTRA 4

Make a triangle

a There are three possible triangles: 2, 3, 4; 2, 4, 5; 3, 4, 5.
(To make a triangle, the sum of the lengths of the two shortest
sticks must be greater than the length of the longest stick.)

b With sticks of length 1 cm–10 cm there are fifty possible
triangles.

EXTRA 5

How many pieces?

a 2 folds, 4 pieces.

b N folds, $N + 2$ pieces.

EXTRA 6

Counting cells

The distance to the moon and back is around $(2 \times 385\,000)$km.

So the distance there and back 8000 times is
$385\,000 \times 2 \times 8000$ km.

There is 2 m of DNA in each cell, so the number of cells in one
human body is $\frac{385\,000 \times 2 \times 8000 \times 1000}{2}$, which is just over 3×10^{12}.

EXTRA 7

Days in the year

a $365 = 169 + 196 = 13^2 + 14^2$;
   $365 = 100 + 121 + 144 = 10^2 + 11^2 + 12^2$.

b $366 = 64 + 81 + 100 + 121 = 8^2 + 9^2 + 10^2 + 11^2$; the only way.

EXTRA 8

Symmetrical years

If the whole number is unchanged by a half turn, then the middle two digits and the outer two digits must also be unchanged by a half turn. The only pairs of digits with this property are $00, 11, 69, 88, 96$. Any combination of these pairs, such as 1881, will work. The next such date is 6009 (then 6119, 6699, 6889, 6969).

COMMENTS & SOLUTIONS

Glossary

- This list of symbols, and of common terms and their meanings, contains the information you need to make sense of the questions and the solutions.
- You may need to refer to a mathematics dictionary or a textbook for more detailed explanations.

Symbols

$a > b$ a is greater than b
$a \geq b$ a is greater than or equal to b
$a < b$ a is less than b
$a \leq b$ a is less than or equal to b
$a = b$ a is equal to b
$a \neq b$ a is not equal to b
$a \approx b$ a is approximately equal to b
^{-}a *minus a*, or the negative of a
$\sqrt{a}$ the square root of a
$a : b$ the ratio of a to b
$a \equiv b$ a is equivalent to b (or a is identically equal to b)
$\therefore$ therefore
$\Rightarrow$ implies that

Terms

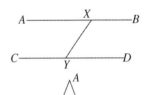

Alternate angles   If AB and CD are *parallel* lines, X lies on AB and Y lies on CD, then $\angle AXY$ and $\angle DYX$ are **alternate angles**: $\angle AXY = \angle DYX$.

Apex   A triangle ABC is *isosceles* with **apex** A if $AB = AC$; the side BC opposite the apex A is called the base of the isosceles triangle.

Base   Integers are usually written in **base** 10, using digits 0, 1, 2, 3, 4, 5, 6, 7, 8, 9. The right-hand *digit* of an integer in **base** 10 counts units, the next position counts tens, the next counts hundreds and so on. In **base** 10, the number twenty four is written **24**, meaning 2 tens and 4 units.

When numbers are written in **base** 3, only the digits 0, 1, 2 are used. The right-hand digit counts units, the next position counts threes, the next position counts nines (since $9 = 3^2$), and so on. In **base** 3, the number twenty four is written **220**, meaning 2 nines, 2 threes and 0 units.

Billion   In the English-speaking world **billion** now means a thousand million, or 10^9. (It used to mean a million million, or 10^{12}, and it still has this meaning in some European languages, such as German.)

Congruent Two triangles ABC and DEF are **congruent** if the sides of the two triangles are equal in pairs ($AB = DE$, $BC = EF$, $CA = FD$), and the angles are also equal in pairs ($\angle ABC = \angle DEF$, $\angle BCA = \angle EFD$, $\angle CAB = \angle FDE$). If two triangles are **congruent**, they have exactly the same size and shape. To show that two triangles ABC and DEF are congruent, it is enough to show

(a) that the three sides are equal in pairs: $AB = DE$, $BC = EF$, $CA = FD$. This is called the **SSS congruence criterion**; or

(b) that two corresponding sides and the included angle are equal: $AB = DE$, $BC = EF$, $\angle CAB = \angle FDE$. This is called the **SAS congruence criterion**.

Consecutive Two integers are **consecutive** if they differ by 1, for example, 4 and 5. Two terms of a number sequence, or two events in a sequence of events, are **consecutive** if one comes immediately after the other.

Decagon A **decagon** is a polygon with ten vertices (and ten edges).

Denominator In the fraction $\frac{3}{4}$, the number on the bottom, 4, is the **denominator**. (The number on the top is the *numerator*.)

Difference The **difference** of two numbers is found by subtracting the smaller number from the larger: for example, the **difference** between $^-2$ and 4 is 6.

Digit A **digit** is one of the numbers 0, 1, 2, 3, 4, 5, 6, 7, 8, 9. The number 1234 has four **digits**: 3 is the tens digit of 1234.

Dimensions The **dimensions** of a rectangle are the two measurements – length and width. The dimensions of a cuboid are the three measurements – length, width and height.

Divisibility test A **divisibility test** (or rule) is a quick way of deciding whether a given number is divisible by a fixed number. For example, a number is exactly divisible by 5 when its units digit is 0 or 5. 63 is **divisible** by 9 (since $63 \div 9 = 7$, with no remainder). 63 is *not* **divisible** by 8 (since $63 \div 8 = 7$ remainder 7).

Equilateral A triangle ABC is **equilateral** if its sides AB, BC, CA are all of equal length.

Equivalent Two different-looking fractions are **equivalent** if they represent the same number. For example, $\frac{2}{3}$ and $\frac{4}{6}$ are **equivalent** fractions.

Even chance If an experiment has two possible outcomes, and each is equally likely, we say that there is an **even chance** of observing either outcome.

Factor 9 is a **factor** of 63, because 63 can be written as '$9 \times$ an integer' ($63 = 9 \times 7$). 9 is *not* a **factor** of 64 because 64 cannot be written as '$9 \times$ an integer'.

Fair A dice is **fair** if each of its faces is equally likely to show when the dice is rolled or thrown. A coin is **fair** if the two possible outcomes, Heads and Tails, are equally likely to occur when the coin is tossed.

Fibonacci sequence	In the **Fibonacci sequence** the first two terms are 1 and 1, and every subsequent term is equal to the sum of the previous two terms: so the third term is $1 + 1 = 2$, and the sequence continues like this: $1, 1, 2, 3, 5, 8, 13, \ldots$.
Fraction	A **fraction** is the number obtained when one integer quantity (the dividend, or *numerator*) is divided by a non-zero integer quantity (the divisor, or *denominator*).
Glossary	A **glossary** is a list of specialist words, together with their meanings.
Hypotenuse	The **hypotenuse** of a right-angled triangle is the side opposite the right angle.
Improper	A fraction which is greater than 1 is **improper** (that is, the numerator is greater than the denominator).
Integer	An **integer** is any whole number, whether positive, negative or zero; for example, $^{-}12$, 0, 5, 746.
Internal angle	An **internal angle** of a polygon $ABCD$ is an angle inside the polygon between two adjacent sides (such as $\angle ABC$).
Isosceles	A triangle ABC is **isosceles** with *apex A* if $AB = AC$; the side BC opposite the apex A is called the *base* of the isosceles triangle.
Kite	A **kite** is a quadrilateral $ABCD$ in which $AB = BC$ and $CD = DA$.
Magic square	A square grid of integers is called a **magic square** if the sum of the numbers along each row, the sum of the numbers down each column, and the sum of the numbers in each of the two diagonals, all give the same answer.
Mean	The **mean** of the five numbers 7, 3, 2, 7, 11 is obtained by adding the five numbers $(7 + 3 + 2 + 7 + 11)$ and then dividing the answer, 30, by the number of numbers in the original list, 5. So the **mean** of the numbers 7, 3, 2, 7, 11 is $30 \div 5 = 6$.
Median	To find the **median** of the five numbers 7, 3, 2, 7, 11, put the numbers in order (2, 3, 7, 7, 11), then choose the middle number, 7. To find the **median** of the six numbers 8, 2, 1, 6, 29, 67, put the numbers in order (1, 2, 6, 8, 29, 67) and choose the mean of the two middle numbers, $(6 + 8)/2 = 7$.
Mixed number	A **mixed number** is a fraction (like $2\frac{3}{4}$), which is written in the form integer $(2) +$ proper fraction $(\frac{3}{4})$.
Non-terminating decimal	A **non-terminating decimal** is a decimal which goes on for ever like $0.123\,123\,123\,123\,123\,123\ldots$ or $1.234\,567\,891\,011\,121\,314\,151\,617\,181\,920\,2\ldots$.

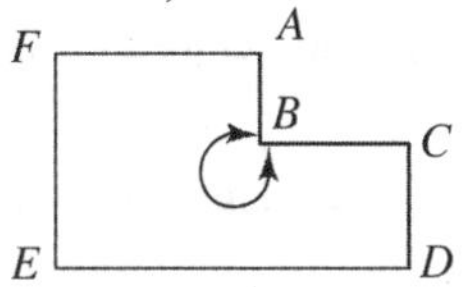

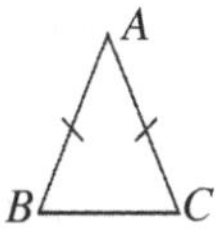

The internal angle diagram shows points F, A at top, B, C to the right, E, D at bottom of a rectangle with an angle arc inside.

The isosceles triangle has apex A at top and base BC at bottom.

Magic square:

2	9	4
7	5	3
6	1	8

GLOSSARY

The first of these examples has a *recurring* block: '123'; the second example has no recurring block.

Numerator In the fraction $\frac{3}{4}$, the number on the top, 3, is the **numerator**. (The number on the bottom is the *denominator*.)

Obtuse An **obtuse** angle is an angle between $90°$ and $180°$.

Order A rectangle has *rotational symmetry* of **order** 2 about its centre P (because it lands up exactly on top of itself when you rotate it through an angle of $360° \div 2$ about the point P). If the rectangle happens to be a square, then it has rotational symmetry of **order** 4 about its centre.

Parallel Two (infinite) straight lines in the plane are **parallel** if they never meet.

Parallelogram A **parallelogram** is a *quadrilateral ABCD* in which the side AB is *parallel* to DC, and the side BC is *parallel* to AD.

Perpendicular Two straight lines are **perpendicular** if they meet at right angles.

Plane A **plane** is a flat surface – that is, a surface in which the straight line joining any two of its points lies wholly in the surface.

Polygon A **polygon** with three vertices (and three sides) is a triangle; a **polygon** with four vertices is a quadrilateral; a **polygon** with five vertices is called a pentagon, one with six vertices is a hexagon, one with eight vertices is an octagon, and one with ten vertices is a decagon.
A **polygon** $ABCDE\ldots M$ is an ordered sequence of points $A, B, C, D, E, \ldots, M$ (called *vertices*) and line segments $AB, BC, CD, DE, \ldots, LM, MA$ (called edges) in the plane, such that any two consecutive edges – such as AB and BC (or MA and AB) – have exactly one vertex in common, and two non-consecutive edges have no points in common at all.

Power A **power** of 10 is a number of the form $10^2 (= 100)$, or $10^3 (= 1000)$, or $10^4 (= 10\,000)$. $10^1 (= 10)$, and $10^0 (= 1)$ are also **powers** of 10. Similarly, a **power** of 2 is a number like $(2^0, $ or $2^1, $ or$)$ 2^2, or $2^3, \ldots$.

Prime number A **prime number** is a positive integer which has exactly two factors – namely itself and 1. 1 is *not* a prime number.

Probability Given a range of possible outcomes for an event, the **probability** of a particular outcome is an exact measure of how likely that outcome is – given by a number between 0 and 1. For example, when tossing a fair coin, there are just two possible outcomes: Heads and Tails. With a fair coin these two outcomes are equally likely, so each outcome has probability exactly $\frac{1}{2}$. An outcome which is completely certain has probability 1; an outcome which is impossible has probability 0.

Product	Given a collection of numbers, their **product** is the number obtained when you multiply them all together. For example, the product of 2, 3, 4 is $2 \times 3 \times 4 = 24$.
Proof	Given any precise logical statement, a **proof** of that statement is a sequence of logically correct steps which shows that the statement is true.
Proper	A fraction which lies between 0 and 1 is **proper**: that is, a fraction is **proper** if it is positive and the numerator is smaller than the denominator.
QED	**QED** is often written to mark the end of a proof. Q, E, and D are the initial letters of the latin clause *Quod Erat Demonstrandum* – meaning 'which is what was to be proved'.
Quadrangle	A **quadrangle** is a polygon with four angles.
Quadrilateral	A **quadrilateral** is a polygon with four sides.
Random	When we call an event **random** it has to be the result of a process which can be repeated over and over again (such as tossing a coin, or choosing a number from a given collection of numbers). The word random then describes not just one particular event or outcome, but rather the unpredictable nature of the underlying process. The process is **random** if, when you use it over and over again to generate a sequence of outcomes, this sequence displays no regularity of any kind. So no matter how much you know about the outcomes which have occurred up to some point, you cannot use this information to predict individual future events in the sequence.
Ratio	The **ratio** of two quantities is given by a pair of numbers separated by a colon which indicates the relative size of the two quantities. For example, the number of white squares □ ■ ■ □ □ and black squares in the diagram are in the **ratio** 3 : 2.
Recurring decimal	A **recurring decimal** is a decimal like that for $\frac{1}{3} = 0.333\,333\ldots$, or $\frac{1}{6} = 0.166\,666\,66\ldots$, or $\frac{1}{7} = 0.142\,857\,142\,857\,142\,857\ldots$, or $\frac{1}{11} = 0.090\,909\,090\,9\ldots$, which goes on for ever, repeating the same string of digits over and over.
Reflection symmetry	A shape has **reflection symmetry** with mirror line m if, when you swap the two parts on either side of the (dotted) mirror, the whole shape lands up exactly on top of itself.
Remainder	10 goes into 23 twice, with **remainder** 3.
Rhombus	A **rhombus** is a *quadrilateral* with all four sides of equal length.

Rotational symmetry	A rectangle has **rotational symmetry** about its centre P (because it lands up exactly on top of itself when you rotate it through $180°$ about the point P). A shape has **rotational symmetry** (or point symmetry) about a point P if it is possible to map it exactly on top of itself by rotating it through some angle less than $360°$ about P.

Rounding	A decimal such as 512.683 can be **rounded** to 1 decimal place as 512.7, or **rounded** to 2 significant figures as 510.
Segment	The line **segment** AB is that part of the infinite line through the two points A and B which lies between A and B (together with the two end points A and B).
Similar	Two shapes are **similar** if they can be labelled so that each segment of one shape is k times as long as the corresponding segment in the other shape, for some fixed k. The two most important consequences of this definition are: (a) two shapes are **similar** if they have exactly the same shape, but may be of different sizes; (b) two triangles ABC, $A'B'C'$ are exactly **similar** when corresponding angles are equal in pairs: $\angle ABC = \angle A'B'C'$, $\angle BCA = \angle B'C'A'$, $\angle CAB = \angle C'A'B'$.
Square	An integer is a **square** (sometimes called a perfect square) if it is equal to the product of some integer by itself; for example, $0 = 0 \times 0$, $1 = 1 \times 1$, $4 = 2 \times 2$. So an integer is a **square** if it is equal to the area of a geometrical square with integer length sides.
Square root	$9 = 3 \times 3$ is the square of 3; 3 is the **square root** of $9 = 3 \times 3$. We use the symbol $\sqrt{\ }$, and write $3 = \sqrt{9}$.
Standard form	A number which is written as a number between 1 and 10 multiplied by a power of 10 is in **standard form**. For example, $525 = 5.25 \times 10^2$.
Sum	The **sum** of 7 and 16 is $23 = 7 + 16$.
Symmetrical	A plane shape is **symmetrical** if it has either *rotational* or *reflection symmetry*.
Tally	A **tally** keeps count by grouping tally marks in fives: $\cancel{||||}\ \cancel{||||}\ |||$
Term	Given a sequence such as $1^2 = 1$, $2^2 = 4$, $3^2 = 9$, $4^2 = 16, \ldots, n^2, \ldots,$ 1 is the first **term**, 4 is the second **term**, and n^2 is the nth **term**.
Terminating decimal	A **terminating decimal** is a decimal which terminates, or stops.
Tesselate	A plane shape **tesselates** the plane if infinitely many copies of the shape can fit together to cover the whole plane, without overlapping and without leaving any gaps.
Trapezium	A **trapezium** is a *quadrilateral* with one pair of parallel edges.

| Triangular number | A **triangular number** is the number of dots in a triangular array like the one shown here. Thus each **triangular number** is given by a sum of the form $1 + 2 + 3 + 4 + \ldots + n$ for some n. | |

Unit fraction   A **unit fraction** is a fraction with numerator 1.

Venn diagram   A **Venn diagram** is a diagram in which circles are drawn to represent different collections of objects; where two circles overlap, the overlapping region is taken to represent precisely those objects which belong in both circles.

Vertex   A **vertex** of a polygon is a point where two adjacent edges meet. A **vertex** of a three dimensional solid is a point where three or more edges meet.

Vertically opposite   If AB and CD are lines which cross at the point X, then $\angle AXC$ and $\angle BXD$ are **vertically opposite** angles: $\angle AXC = \angle BXD$.